Under the Midnight Stars

HBJ HARCOURT BRACE JOVANOVICH, PUBLISHERS
Orlando   San Diego   Chicago   Dallas

Under the Midnight Stars

ODYSSEY An HBJ Literature Program
Second Edition

Sam Leaton Sebesta

Consultants

Elaine M. Aoki   Myra Cohn Livingston

Willard E. Bill   Daphne P. Muse

Sonya Blackman   Sandra McCandless Simons

Sylvia Engdahl   Barre Toelken

Acknowledgments

For permission to reprint copyrighted material, grateful acknowledgment is made to the following sources:

Addison-Wesley Publishing Company: The poem "I Am Rose" from *The World Is Round* by Gertrude Stein. © 1966 by Addison-Wesley, Reading, Massachusetts.

Atheneum Publishers: "Mean Song" from *There Is No Rhyme for Silver* by Eve Merriam. Copyright © 1962 by Eve Mer-riam. " 'Let's Marry!' Said the Cherry" with accompanying illustrations from *Let's Marry Said the Cherry and Other Non-sense Poems* by N. M. Bodecker (A Margaret K. McElderry Book). Copyright © 1974 by N. M. Bodecker. Illustration accompanying "The Fly in the Rye" from *Let's Marry Said the Cherry and Other Nonsense Poems* by N. M. Bodecker (A Margaret K. McElderry Book). Copyright © 1974 by N. M. Bodecker.

Blackie and Son Limited: Text from "Twelve Months" from *Russian Fairy Tales* by Moura Budberg et al.

William Collins Publishers, Inc., Philomel Books and Jane Yolen: Adapted text and illustrations from *The Emperor and the Kite* by Jane Yolen, illustrated by Ed Young. Copyright © 1967 by Jane Yolen; illustrations copyright © 1967 by Ed Young; copyright © 1967 by the World Publishing Company.

Harold Courlander and George Herzog: "Talk" from *The Cow-Tail Switch and Other West African Stories* by Harold Cour-lander and George Herzog. © 1947, 1975 by Holt, Rinehart and Winston; © 1981 by Harold Courlander and George Herzog.

Delacorte Press: Excerpted from *Panda* by Susan Bonners. Copyright © 1978 by Susan Bonners.

Doubleday & Company, Inc.: Adapted from *Amelia's Flying Machine* by Barbara Shook Hazen. Copyright © 1977 by Barbara Shook Hazen. "I Go Forth to Move About the Earth" by Alonzo Lopez from *The Whispering Wind,* edited by Terry Allen. Copyright © 1972 by the Institute of American Indian Arts.

E. P. Dutton: "Winter Walk" from *Street Poems* by Robert Froman. Copyright © 1971 by Robert Froman.

Miriam Farber, on behalf of the heirs of Norma Farber: "Spend-thrift" by Norma Farber. © 1976 by Norma Farber.

Four Winds Press, a division of Scholastic Magazines, Inc.: From *Rumpelstiltskin,* retold by Edith H. Tarcov, illustrated by Edward Gorey. Text copyright © 1973 by Edith H. Tarcov; illustrations copyright © 1973 by Edward Gorey.

Grosset & Dunlap, Inc.: "A very fat snowman" from *The Big Book of Limericks* by Edward Mullins. Copyright © 1968 by Edward Mullins. Published by Platt & Munk.

Harcourt Brace Jovanovich, Inc.: "The Big Wind of '34," abridged and slightly adapted from *Grandpa's Farm* by James Flora. © 1965 by James Flora. Excerpt from *Rufus M* by Eleanor Estes. Copyright 1943, 1971 by Eleanor Estes. "Theme in Yellow" from *Chicago Poems* by Carl Sandburg. Copyright 1916 by Holt, Rinehart and Winston, Inc.; copy-right 1944 by Carl Sandburg. "Winter Night" from *The Golden Hive* by Harry Behn. Copyright © 1962, 1966 by Harry Behn.

Harper & Row, Publishers, Inc.: Adaptation of the text of *Wolfie* by Janet Chenery. Text copyright © 1969 by Janet Dai Chenery. Adaptation of the text of *Old Arthur* by Liesel Moak Skorpen. Text copyright © 1972 by Liesel Moak Skorpen. "Spring" from *Dogs & Dragons, Trees & Dreams: A Col-lection of Poems* by Karla Kuskin. Copyright © 1968 by Karla Kuskin. Adaptation of the text of *Sparrow Socks* by George Selden. Text copyright © 1965 by George S. Thompson. "Gently, gently . . ." from *I See the Winds* by Kazue Mizumura (Thomas Y. Crowell Co.) Copyright © 1966 by Kazue Mizumura. Illustration from *Stevie* by John Steptoe. Copyright © 1969 by John L. Steptoe.

Houghton Mifflin Company and George Allen & Unwin Ltd.: From "Oliphaunt" in *The Adventures of Tom Bombadil* by J. R. R. Tolkien. Copyright © 1962 by George Allen & Unwin Ltd.

Alfred A. Knopf, Inc.: From *The Cat Came Back* by Dahlov Ipcar. Copyright © 1971 by Dahlov Ipcar. "In Time of Silver Rain" from *Selected Poems* by Langston Hughes. Copy-right 1938; renewed 1966 by Langston Hughes.

Ray Lincoln Literary Agency, 4 Surrey Road, Melrose Park, PA 19126, U.S.A.: "Eat–It–All–Elaine" from *Don't Ever Cross A Crocodile* by Kaye Starbird. © 1963 by Kaye Starbird. Published by J. B. Lippincott Company.

Little, Brown and Company: From "Adventures of Isabel" in *Custard and Company* by Ogden Nash. Copyright 1935 by Ogden Nash. "The Grasshopper" from *Far and Few* by David McCord. Copyright 1952 by David McCord. Text only from *Just the Thing for Geraldine* by Ellen Conford. Copyright © 1974 by Ellen Conford.

Little, Brown and Company in association with the Atlantic Monthly Press: Mississippi Possum by Miska Miles. Copyright © 1965 by Miska Miles.

Macmillan Publishing Company: From "Something Told the Wild Geese" in *Poems* by Rachel Field. Copyright 1934 by Macmillan Publishing Co., Inc.; renewed © 1962 by Arthur S. Pederson. Text from *The Tales of Olga Da Polga* by Michael Bond. Copyright © 1971 by Michael Bond.

Macmillan Publishing Co., Inc.: "March" from *Summer Green* by Elizabeth Coatsworth. Copyright 1948 by Macmillan Publishing Co., Inc.; renewed 1976 by Elizabeth Coatsworth Beston. "The Bear" and "Patsy Again" (Retitled: "Maurice's Bear") from *Maurice's Room* by Paula Fox. Copyright © 1966 by Paula Fox.

Macmillan Publishing Co., Inc. and Macmillan, London and Basingstoke: "Paper Boats" from "The Crescent Moon" in *Collected Poems and Plays* by Rabindranath Tagore. Copyright 1913 by Macmillan Publishing Co., Inc.; renewed 1941 by Rabindranath Tagore.

Playboy Magazine: "Not Me" by Shel Silverstein. Copyright © 1960 by Shel Silverstein. Originally appeared in *Playboy* Magazine.

G. P. Putnam's Sons: "The Beach" from *The Adventures of Mole & Troll* by Tony Johnston, illustrated by Wallace Tripp. Text copyright © 1972 by Tony Johnston; illustrations copyright © 1972 by Wallace Tripp.

Random House, Inc.: From *My Father's Dragon* (Retitled: "My Father and the Dragon") by Ruth Stiles Gannett. Copyright 1948 by Random House, Inc.

Marian Reiner: "Discovery" from *Whispers and Other Poems* by Myra Cohn Livingston. Copyright © 1958, 1978 by Myra Cohn Livingston.

Marian Reiner, agent for the author: "Fourth of July" by Myra Cohn Livingston appears here for the first time. Copyright © 1986 by Myra Cohn Livingston.

Scott, Foresman and Company: "Fall" by Sally Andresen from *Reflections on a Gift of Watermelon Pickle* by Stephen Dunning, Edward Lueders and Hugh Smith. Copyright © 1966 by Scott, Foresman and Company.

Viking Penguin Inc.: From *Along Sandy Trails*, text by Ann Nolan Clark and photographs by Alfred A. Cohn. Text copyright © 1969 by Ann Nolan Clark; photographs copyright © 1969 by Alfred A. Cohn. All rights reserved.

Frederick Warne & Company, Inc.: Adapted excerpt from *Dance of the Animals*, retold by Pura Belpre. Copyright © 1972 by Pura Belpre.

Art Acknowledgments

Willi K. Baum: 271 left; Chuck Bowden: 154, 197, 251, 269 (adapted from photographs from the following sources: 154, courtesy UPI; 197, courtesy Harcourt Brace Jovanovich, Inc.; 251, courtesy Pura Belpré); Diane de Groat: 133; Bert Dodson: 154–155, 156; Sharon Harker: 40, 41, 42, 134, 135 top, 136–137 top, 270–271 top, 272 top; Ed Taber: 270 bottom, 271 right, 272 bottom; Jack Wallen: 32, 55, 133, 179, 211, 365; Don Weller: 292.

Cover: Tom Leonard

Maps: Joanna Adamska Koperska

Unit Openers: Jane Teiko Oka

Contents

10

1 One of a Kind

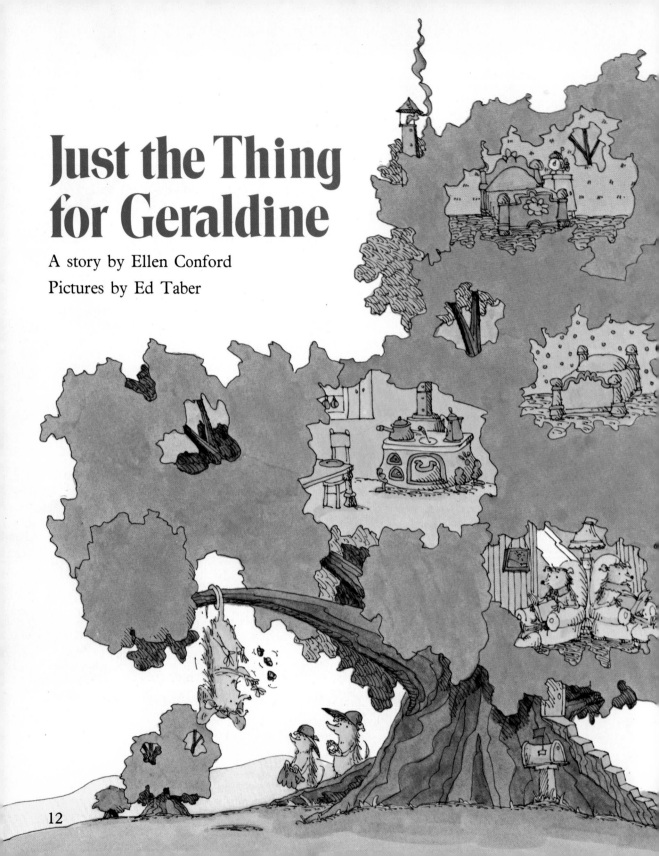

Just the Thing for Geraldine

A story by Ellen Conford

Pictures by Ed Taber

Geraldine the possum lives with her parents and her brothers Eugene and Randolph in a big, old tree. Geraldine can often be found there, hanging from a tree branch and juggling.

There was nothing Geraldine liked better than hanging by her tail from the branch of a tree and juggling a few acorns.

But her parents told her there was more to life than juggling, so every week she went to Mademoiselle La Fay's School of the Dance to learn ballet.

"It will help you to be graceful," said her mother.

"It will help you to be ladylike," said her father.

"It will help you keep physically fit," said her brother Randolph.

"Nothing could help her," whispered her brother Eugene.

One day Geraldine came home from ballet school very excited.

"Everybody come look!" she shouted. "Come look at what I can do!"

"What is it?" asked her mother.

"We learned the Dance of the Purple Swan," Geraldine said.

"That's wonderful!" said her mother.

"A whole dance!" exclaimed her father. "And you haven't even been going to dancing school very long."

"Swans aren't purple," said Eugene.

"Now, watch me," Geraldine ordered. "Are you looking?"

"We're looking," said her mother.

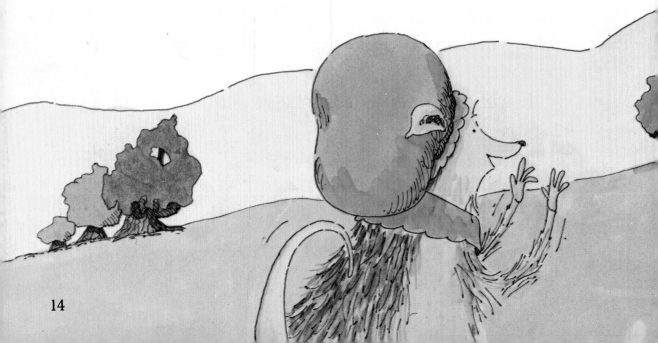

Geraldine smoothed down her tutu,
which her mother had made for her out of
leaves, and gracefully raised her forepaws
over her head.

"Dee, da da da da dee ta dum," she
hummed, and ran lightly, on tiptoe, around
the trunk of the tree.

"Oh, how beautiful," sighed her mother.

"Encore, encore!" clapped her father.

"That's pretty good, Geraldine," said
Randolph.

"Can we go play now?" asked Eugene.

"Dee, da da da da ta dum," Geraldine hummed, and began to dance faster around the tree.

But one of the big roots of the tree was sticking up from the ground and Geraldine didn't see it.

"Ow!" yelled Geraldine, as she tripped over the root and sprawled on the ground.

"Did you hurt yourself?" asked her mother worriedly.

"No," Geraldine sniffled, and ran up the tree before Randolph and Eugene could see her tears. She hung upside down by her tail, her leafy ballet skirt covering her face.

"I see you, Randolph," she said angrily. "You think I can't see you, but I can. You'd better stop laughing."

Randolph covered his mouth with his paw.

"I'm not laughing," he said, trying to sound serious.

"Is it all right if *I* laugh?" asked Eugene.

"There is nothing to laugh at," their father said sternly.

"Geraldine just tripped," their mother said. "It could happen to anyone."

"Especially Geraldine," whispered Eugene to Randolph.

"I heard you, Eugene!" Geraldine shouted. "You think I can't hear you, but I can!" She pulled herself back up on the branch and straightened her tutu. "I'd like to see *you* do the Dance of the Purple Swan."

"Swans aren't purple," said Eugene. "Swans are white."

Randolph and Eugene went back to their game. Geraldine took off her ballet skirt. She looked at it thoughtfully as she folded it and put it away.

The following week, when Geraldine came home from ballet school, her mother and father were waiting for her.

"Well, what did you learn at dancing school today?" her mother asked eagerly.

"I learned," Geraldine said unhappily, "that I am not a very good dancer."

"Nonsense!" said her father. "You dance beautifully. And you haven't even been going to dancing school very long."

"And I don't think I'll be going much longer," said Geraldine.

"Oh, of course you will," said her mother. "You'll see, you'll be a graceful dancer in no time."

Geraldine shook her head.

"No, I won't," she said. "I cannot do *pliés* and *arabesques,* and when we're supposed to dance on our toes my toes curl up and I fall down. I am just not cut out for ballet."

"But I thought you liked ballet school," said her mother.

"I like juggling better," said Geraldine.

"But don't you want to learn to be graceful?" asked her father.

"No," said Geraldine, swinging back and forth by her tail from the branch of the tree and juggling some pebbles. "Not really."

"Oh," said her mother.

So, her mother signed her up for a class at Schuyler's School of Sculpture.

"I'm sure you have artistic talent," said her mother.

"Sculpture school is just the thing for you, Geraldine," agreed her father.

"I don't know," said Geraldine, doubtfully, as she flipped three blackberries in the air and balanced a twig on the end of her nose.

"Oh, you'll see," said her mother. "You'll make bowls and pitchers and artistic statues. Sculpture school will be lots of fun."

Every week Geraldine went to Schuyler's School of Sculpture, and every week her parents asked, "How do you like sculpture school?"

And every week Geraldine shrugged and said, "It's okay, I guess."

One day Geraldine came home from class carrying a big pile of something wrapped in wet leaves.

"What's that?" asked Randolph.

"That's clay," said Geraldine.

"What's it for?" asked Eugene curiously.

"We have to make a sculpture of someone," Geraldine said.

"Oh, boy!" cried Eugene, jumping up and standing very straight and flexing his muscles. "Do me, Geraldine, do me!"

"We just have to do the head," Geraldine said.

"Oh," said Eugene, disappointed. "Well," he brightened a minute later, "do *my* head." He turned his head sideways so Geraldine could see his profile. "I have a nice head. Please, Geraldine?"

"You have to sit very still," Geraldine warned. "You can't move around or wiggle or anything."

"I won't," promised Eugene. "I won't even blink."

Geraldine sat Eugene down in front of her and turned his head sideways. She unwrapped the mound of clay and put it on a tree stump. Randolph sat down next to her.

"Don't sit there and watch me!" Geraldine snapped. "How do you expect me to concentrate when you're staring at me like that?"

"You're very touchy," said Randolph. "Why are you in such a bad mood?"

"I'm not in a bad mood!" yelled Geraldine. "Now, go away and leave me alone!"

Randolph went off to play ball and Geraldine began to work on her sculpture.

After a while, Eugene began to squirm.

"Is it finished yet, Geraldine?" he asked.

"No," said Geraldine.

"My nose itches," complained Eugene.

"Sit still and be quiet!" Geraldine ordered.

Geraldine molded the clay, squeezing it, poking it, and muttering to herself while she worked.

"What are you saying, Geraldine?"
Eugene asked. "I can't hear you."

"I'm saying 'stupid clay!' " Geraldine
snapped. "Now will you be still? How can
I sculpt you if you keep wriggling around?"

"I can't help it," Eugene whined. "I'm
getting tired. My neck hurts. And I think I
have to sneeze."

"Be quiet. And I'm doing your mouth
now, so please keep it shut."

Eugene sighed. Geraldine went on
molding and muttering.

Finally she said, "There. It's done. I
think."

"Oh, good!" said Eugene, jumping up and stretching. "I feel stiff all over. Let's see it."

But Geraldine was covering her sculpture with the wet leaves.

"Let me see it," Eugene said. "Why are you covering it up? I want to see my head."

He ran over to the tree stump and began pulling off the leaves.

"Stop it!" yelled Geraldine, swatting at him. "You stop that, Eugene! I don't want you to look at it. I don't want *anybody* to look at it."

"I won't hurt it," Eugene said, yanking off the leaves. "I want to see it."

Randolph and their mother and father came running when they heard Eugene and Geraldine.

"What's going on?" asked their father.

"Why are you two screaming like this?" asked their mother.

"*What* is *that?*" Randolph asked, pointing toward the tree stump.

Eugene had pulled all the leaves off Geraldine's sculpture and was backing away from the tree stump, shaking his head in fury.

"That is *not* me!" he howled. "I don't look like that!"

"Well, if you didn't move around so much—" Geraldine shouted.

"Is *that* supposed to be *Eugene?*" Randolph asked.

"It's . . . it's very interesting," their father said weakly.

"It is not interesting!" shrieked Eugene. "It's a bunch of lumps! I don't look like a bunch of lumps!"

Geraldine sighed, and began to cover up
her sculpture with leaves again. When she
finished covering it all up, she climbed the
tree and hung by her tail, swinging gently
back and forth as she juggled some pine
cones.

A little while later Randolph and
Eugene came up the tree and sat down next
to Geraldine.

"You sure are a good juggler, Geraldine,"
said Randolph kindly.

"Thank you," Geraldine murmured.

Randolph gave Eugene a poke in the ribs.

"Ow! I mean, oh," said Eugene, "I wish
I could juggle like you can."

"Do you really?" Geraldine asked.

"You're the best juggler we know. ISN'T THAT RIGHT, EUGENE?" said Randolph, glaring at his brother.

"Yes," Eugene said.

"So we'd like you to teach us how to juggle," Randolph said. "WOULDN'T WE, EUGENE?"

"Yes," Eugene said.

"Oh," said Geraldine, happily, "of course I'll teach you. It's not too hard, once you get the hang of it. Now, just watch me and——"

"Geraldine!" her mother called. "I've thought of just the thing for you!"

"What is it?" asked Geraldine.

"Singing lessons!" her mother said excitedly. "How would you like to take singing lessons?"

"No," said Geraldine, juggling her acorns.

"No?" her father asked. "But you'd love singing lessons."

"No," repeated Geraldine. "I wouldn't."

"But, why not, Geraldine?" asked her mother.

"What if I'm not a good singer?" said Geraldine. "I took ballet lessons and found out I wasn't a good dancer."

"And you certainly aren't good at sculpting," Eugene added.

"She sure is a good juggler, though," said Randolph. "And nobody ever gave her juggling lessons."

"That's true," their mother said.

"I never thought of that," said their father.

"Neither did I," said Geraldine.

Suddenly, she stopped juggling and jumped up.

"I'll be right back," she said, and ran down the tree.

In a little while, Geraldine returned. She was lugging a big piece of wood.

"What's that?" asked Randolph.

Geraldine propped the wood up against the trunk of the tree.

"Come and look," she said proudly.

The possums came down from the tree.

"I made a sign," said Geraldine.

"What kind of a sign?" asked Eugene. "What does it say?"

"Oh, it's beautiful," said their mother.

"Aren't you the clever one!" said their father.

"What does it *say?*" cried Eugene. "Tell me what it says!"

"It says," Randolph told him, "GERALDINE'S JUGGLING SCHOOL."

GERALDINE'S JUGGLING SCHOOL

Questions

1. What was funny to Eugene but *not* funny to Geraldine?

2. "Why should my daughter go to juggling school? What good is juggling?" asked Sarah Squirrel's father. Tell what Geraldine answered.

3. Geraldine had a *talent* for juggling. What is a *talent?*
   a. a wish to learn something
   b. an ability to do something well
   c. a pile of acorns and pine cones

4. If Geraldine grows up and has children, what might she tell them about talents?
   a. "Use your talent for juggling."
   b. "Everyone should learn to dance."
   c. "Find your own talents and use them."

Activity   Make a Sign

If you started a school, what would you teach best? Draw or paint a sign for your school. Your sign should tell the name of your school and what you will teach.

"Let's Marry!" Said the Cherry

Poem and pictures by N. M. Bodecker

"Let's marry,"
said the cherry.

"Why me?"
said the pea.

"'Cause you're sweet,"
said the beet.

"Say you will,"
said the dill.

"Think it over,"
said the clover.

"Don't rush,"
said the squash.

"Here's your dress,"
said the cress.

"White and green,"
said the bean.

"And your cape,"
said the grape.

"Trimmed with fur,"
said the burr.

"Won't that tickle?"
said the pickle.

"Who knows?"
said the rose.

"Where's the chapel?"
said the apple.

"In Greenwich,"
said the spinach.

"We'll be there!"
said the pear.

"Wearing what?"
said the nut.

"Pants and coats,"
said the oats.

"Shoes and socks,"
said the phlox.

"Shirt and tie,"
said the rye.

"We'll look jolly,"
said the holly.

"You'll look silly,"
said the lily.

"You're crazy,"
said the daisy.

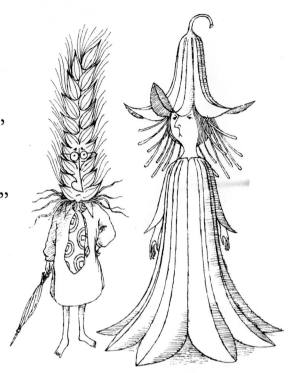

"Come, let's dine,"
said the vine.

"Yeah—let's eat!"
said the wheat.

"And get stout,"
said the sprout.

"Just wait,"
said the date.

"Who will chime?"
said the lime.

"I'll chime!"
said the thyme.

"Who will preach?"
said the peach.

"It's my turn!"
said the fern.

"You would ramble,"
said the bramble.

"Here they come!"
cried the plum.

"Start the tune!"
cried the prune.

"All together!"
cried the heather.

"Here we go!"
said the sloe.

"NOW—let's marry!"
said the cherry.

"Why me?"
said the pea.

"Oh, my gosh!"
said the squash.

"Start all over,"
said the clover.

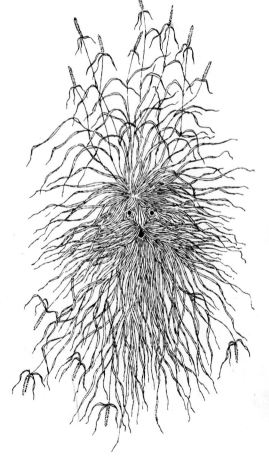

"NO WAY!"
said the hay.

Learn About

Rhyming Couplets by Myra Cohn Livingston

When two things or two friends go together, you can call them a couple. In poetry, when two lines that rhyme go together, they are called a *rhyming couplet* (KUHP•lit). The sound that ends the first line is repeated in the second line. Rhyming couplets are fun to hear, and they are easy to remember.

Here are two rhyming couplets from the poem "'Let's Marry!' Said the Cherry" by N. M. Bodecker.

This is a rhyming couplet.

This is a rhyming couplet, too.

"Let's marry,"
said the cherry.

"Why me?"
said the pea.

In the first couplet, the word that ends the first line is *marry.* It rhymes with *cherry,* the last word in the second line. What are the rhyming words in the second couplet?

Poets often use rhyming couplets in their poems. Some are long poems. Some are short. Gertrude Stein uses only two couplets in her poem "I Am Rose."

I am Rose my eyes are blue
I am Rose and who are you?
I am Rose and when I sing
I am Rose like anything.

Blue and *you* are the rhyming words in the first couplet. What are the rhyming words in the second couplet?

Rules for a Rhyming Couplet

1. Two lines must come one after the other.
2. The end words of both lines must rhyme.

Remember these rules!

Read these poems. Which ones have rhyming couplets? What are the rhyming words?

1. **Discovery**

    Round and round and round I spin
    Making a circle so I can fall in.
    —Myra Cohn Livingston

2. A peanut sat on a railroad track,
    His heart was all a-flutter.
    The five-fifteen came rushing by—
    Toot! toot! peanut butter!
    —An American folk rhyme

3. "What's the news of the day,
    Good neighbor, I pray?"
    "They say the balloon
    Has gone up to the moon!"
    —An old rhyme

Try writing some rhyming couplets yourself. Begin with two couplets. Then perhaps you'll try writing a longer poem.

Mean Song

A poem by Eve Merriam

Snickles and podes,
Ribble and grodes:
That's what I wish you.

A nox in the groot,
A root in the stoot
And a gock in the forbeshaw, too.

Keep out of sight
For fear that I might
Glom you a gravely snave.

Don't show your face
Around any place
Or you'll get one flack snack in the bave.

Picture by Susan Jaekel

The Beach

A play adapted from the story by Tony Johnston
Pictures by Wallace Tripp

Characters

Storyteller 1   **Storyteller 2**   **Mole**   **Troll**

Storyteller 1: Mole and Troll went to the beach.
They felt the warm sand
between their toes.

Storyteller 2: They felt the warm sun on their backs.
When it got too hot,
they sat by the tide pools
and dangled their toes in the water.

Storyteller 1: Suddenly, Mole jumped up!

Mole: You pinched me!

Troll: I did not!
I was sitting here dangling my toes
and minding my own business.

Mole: Well, maybe your business is pinching.
There is no one else around.

Storyteller 2: Troll made a face. He did not like
being called a pincher.
No one said anything for a little while.

Storyteller 1: Then Troll felt a pinch on his toe.

Troll: OU-OU-CH! Stop that pinching, Mole.
Just because someone pinches you,
you do not have to pinch me!

Mole: I did not touch you!

Troll: You did! You did! You *did!*
There is no one else around.

Mole: Look, Troll, it is too nice a day
for arguing.
Let's enjoy the sea
and forget this silliness.

Storyteller 2: So they sat and enjoyed the sea.
The salt mist touched them and felt cool.
Sea gulls flew by,
and everything was calm.

Storyteller 1: Then Mole cried out.

Mole: YI-I-IKES!
You did it again, you fuzzy troll!

Storyteller 2: Troll felt a pinch, too.

Troll: It was you!
This time you pinched me so hard,
you made a little red lump. Look!

Storyteller 1: Mole leaned over to look
and there was a little red lump.

Mole: I did not do that. You have a hive.

Troll: How can I have just one hive?
Hives come in bunches!

Mole: I don't know! But you do!

Troll: All right, we will sit very still
with our hands on our heads
and *see* which one is pinching.

Mole: You are sneaky,
because then you will pinch
with your feet.

Troll: Then we will sit very still
with our hands on our heads
and our feet in plain sight.

Mole: Okay, Troll. We will do that.
But I am sitting on seaweed
to protect myself on all sides.

Troll: Then so am I.

Storyteller 2:   So they sat very still
on big seaweed piles
with their hands on their heads
and their feet in plain sight
to see who was pinching.
They sat like that for a long time.

Storyteller 1: At last Mole said,

Mole: Troll! It is too still.
Nothing is happening.
There is something funny about this.

Storyteller 2: Someone else thought it was funny, too.
Someone else giggled very loudly.

Storyteller 1: It was a big crab.
He had been doing the pinching.
They looked so silly
that he could not help giggling.
Mole and Troll chased him,
but he ran into a tight hole
and giggled for half an hour.

Troll: Mole, I am sorry for shouting at you.

Mole: Me, too. And I would never pinch you, because you are my friend.

Troll: Me, too.

Storyteller 2: Then they went swimming in a place where there were no crabs at all.

Questions

1. Why were Mole and Troll arguing?

2. What did Mole say that made Troll angry?
   a. "Let's enjoy the sea."
   b. "I did not touch you."
   c. "I am sitting on seaweed."

3. What did Mole and Troll do to find out who was doing the pinching?

4. What do you think Mole and Troll should do the next time they argue?

5. What did Mole and Troll do that showed they were happy with each other again?

6. Mole said that Troll had a *hive.* What is a *hive* in this play? What is a *hive* to a bee?

Activity   Write Mole and Troll's Words

Suppose Mole and Troll did not hear the crab giggle. Tell how they could settle their argument. On a piece of paper, write what Mole and Troll might say to each other.

Wolfie

A story by Janet Chenery

Pictures by Dan Siculan

Harry and George sat in their secret meeting place. It was a large doghouse for Harry's dog. But Biffy never used it, so Harry and George did.

"How many flies did you catch?" asked Harry.

"Three," said George. He pulled a small bottle out of his pocket.

"Only three?" asked Harry. "We will need more than that."

George sighed. "It took me an hour to catch these. Are you sure he likes flies?"

"Sure," said Harry. "Don't you remember? The book said that spiders eat live flies and other insects."

"Yes," said George. "But the spider in the picture had a web. Wolfie hasn't made a web yet."

"He will make a web when he sees the flies," Harry said. He picked up a big jar. Something inside it moved. "Hello, Wolfie," Harry whispered. He unscrewed the jar lid carefully. "Get ready," he told George.

George turned his bottle upside down over the big jar. He took off the bottle top and shook the flies into the jar.

Harry quickly put the lid back on. "Have a fly, Wolfie," said Harry.

They watched the brown spider in the jar. At first it did not move. Then it made a dash at the fly. But the fly got away just in time.

Outside the doghouse someone called, "Harry!"

"Shh! It's Polly," Harry whispered. "Hide Wolfie!"

Polly was Harry's little sister. "I want to see the spider," she said.

"No!" said Harry. "Go away! Scram!"

"Wait, Harry," George said. Then he stuck his head out of the doghouse. He said to Polly, "You can see Wolfie. But first you have to bring him a hundred flies. Live ones."

"Okay," said Polly, and off she ran.

"Why did you tell her that?" asked Harry. "Now she'll pester us all the time."

"No, she won't," said George. "It's very hard to catch flies."

"You don't know Polly," Harry grumbled.

They watched Wolfie for a while to see if he would eat the flies.

"Wolfie looks sad," said George. "Maybe we need a bigger place to keep him."

"Let's ask my mother if she has anything bigger," Harry said.

Polly was at the kitchen table. She had a rubber band over her first finger. She pulled the rubber band back like a slingshot. A fly walked across the table. *Snap!* Polly let the rubber band go. The fly bounced over on its back.

"Wow!" said George.

Polly picked up the fly and put it into a jelly jar. There were four other flies in the jar.

"They have to be alive," said Harry. "Wolfie won't eat dead flies."

"They are alive," said Polly. "They are just stunned." She shook the jar. The flies buzzed.

Harry gave George a dirty look. "What did I tell you," he said. Harry asked his mother, "Do you have anything bigger than a jar for Wolfie?"

"Who is Wolfie?" his mother asked.

"He is a big hairy spider," said Harry.

"Harry won't let me see him," Polly said, "until I catch a hundred flies."

"A spider!" said Harry's mother. "Where is it?"

"In Biffy's house," said Polly.

Harry's mother said, "Why don't you take it to Miss Rose at the Nature Center? Biffy and Inky are enough pets for one family."

"Anybody can have a dog and a cat," Harry said.

Polly snapped her rubber band and stunned another fly. "Can I go to the Nature Center, too?" Polly asked.

"No!" said Harry. He and George ran outdoors.

The Nature Center had rocks, butterflies, other insects, and leaves. When they got there, George said, "Miss Rose, do you have something we can keep Wolfie in?"

"Who is Wolfie?" asked Miss Rose.

"Wolfgang," Harry said. "He is a wolf spider."

"Really?" Miss Rose asked. "How do you know?"

"We looked him up in a book," George said.

"He's big and brown and hairy," said Harry. "And he runs very fast. We saw him chase a bug, and he caught it, too."

"What are you feeding him?" Miss Rose asked.

"Flies," George said. "But they are very hard to catch."

"What about water?" asked Miss Rose.

"Water?" asked Harry. "Do spiders drink water?"

"Yes, they need water as much as they need food," said Miss Rose.

"I don't think he's very hungry," George said. "He hasn't made a web to catch flies."

"He won't spin a web if he is a wolf spider," said Miss Rose. "Some spiders spin webs to trap insects, but wolf spiders run after them. They are hunters. Wolf spiders do not trap insects in a web."

"Then what should we keep him in?" asked Harry.

"The best thing would be a big box with a wire screen over the top," Miss Rose said. She showed them what to do.

Miss Rose picked up a small screen. "Here," she said. "You can use this. When you have Wolfie all fixed up, will you bring him here? I'd like to see him."

"Okay," Harry said. "Thank you."

When Harry and George got home, they found an old wooden box. They put some dirt in it. They added twigs and leaves and a little clump of grass. While Harry held the screen, George dumped Wolfie into his new home. Wolfie ran into a corner and hid under a leaf.

"Let's get him some food," said Harry.

"And water," said George.

"How do you give spiders water?" asked Harry.

"I know," said a voice. It was Polly. She was sitting on the grass with Biffy and Inky.

"Go away!" said Harry.

"How *do* you give water to a spider?" asked George.

"You put drops of water on a leaf," Polly said. "Sometimes Inky drinks dewdrops that way."

"Okay, go get water," Harry said.

"Bring some flies, too," George said.

Polly brought back a jar of flies and a glass of water. "I got seven flies," she said. "Can I watch you feed Wolfie?"

"No," said Harry. "You have to get a whole hundred."

George and Harry put the flies into
Wolfie's box. They sprinkled water on the
leaves. Wolfie turned around. One of his
legs touched a wet leaf. He seemed to be
breathing heavily. He bent his knees. Then
he touched the wet leaf.

"He's drinking the water!" George said.

Wolfie made a dash at a fly.

"He got him!" Harry shouted. "Boy, is
he fast!"

The next day Harry and George took Wolfie to Miss Rose.

"You were right," Miss Rose said. "It is a wolf spider. Did you notice how many eyes he has?"

"Eyes?" said George. "Don't insects have two eyes?"

"A spider is not an insect," Miss Rose said.

"What is it then?" Harry asked.

"An *arachnid* (uh•RAK•nid)," said Miss Rose. "Most wolf spiders have eight eyes. Bring him over to my worktable, and I will show you."

George and Harry took Wolfie's box to the table. Miss Rose got a magnifying glass and held it over the spider. He looked enormous, very hairy, and quite cross. Harry counted. Wolfie had eight eyes.

Miss Rose reached into a glass tank and picked up a shiny black beetle. It waved its legs. Miss Rose took the magnifying glass and held it over the beetle so Harry and George could see it.

"How many legs does the beetle have?"
she asked.

Harry and George counted. "Six!" they
said together.

"How many does Wolfie have?" Miss
Rose asked.

"Those two things near his head—are
they his legs?" asked George.

"No, those are palps," said Miss Rose.
"Wolfie sometimes uses them to hold his
food."

"Well then, he has eight legs," Harry
said.

"Right," said Miss Rose. "Spiders have
eight legs. Insects have six."

"Is that what makes spiders and insects different?" asked George. "Just the number of legs?"

"No," said Miss Rose. "There are other differences. Take a good look at Wolfie. How many parts does his body have?"

"He's got a head," said Harry.

"And a body," George added.

"Now look at the beetle," said Miss Rose. "How many parts does it have?" The beetle wriggled in her fingers.

"He has a head, but his body has two parts," said George.

"So he has three parts altogether," said Harry.

"He has feelers on his head, too," said George. "Wolfie doesn't have feelers."

"That's right," Miss Rose said.

"Those don't seem like very big differences," said Harry. "How else are they different?"

Miss Rose put the beetle down gently in its glass box. "Look again," she said. She put the wire screen back over the top.

"Why did we put screens over Wolfie's box and my beetle's tank?" asked Miss Rose.

"So they can have air but can't get out," Harry said.

"How would they get out?" asked Miss Rose.

"Why, Wolfie would climb right out," Harry said.

"The beetle would, too," George said. "Or he could fly out—"

"That's it!" cried Harry. "Wolfie can't fly! He doesn't have wings."

"Right you are, Harry," said Miss Rose. "Spiders don't have wings, but many insects do."

Harry and George took Wolfie back to the doghouse. Every day they watched him and fed him the flies that Polly caught. One day she caught seven, and another day she caught five. But she did not catch anywhere near a hundred.

So Polly asked Harry again, "Can't I see Wolfie now? I have twenty-seven flies."

"No," said Harry. "One hundred."

"Why?" Polly asked. "You showed him to Miss Rose. She didn't catch any flies for him."

"Of course not!" Harry said. "Miss Rose knows all about spiders! Besides, she's not a pest like you!"

"I am *not* a pest," cried Polly.

"Yes, you are," Harry said. "Go away, pest."

Polly did not catch any more flies for Wolfie that day.

When Polly went to bed, she was still mad at Harry. Inky jumped on her bed. "Harry is mean," she told Inky. "Who wants to see his old spider anyway?" she said.

In the middle of the night Polly woke up. She thought about Wolfie and the flies she had to catch before Harry would let her see him. Inky woke up and meowed softly. Polly slipped out of bed and got her flashlight. Inky followed her. They tiptoed out of the room, down the stairs, and out the back door. Silently, they crossed the yard to the doghouse.

Polly shined her flashlight inside. She crawled in and held the light over Wolfie's box. "Hello, Wolfie," she whispered.

Harry woke up, too. The moon made shadows in his room. The shadows looked like big animals with long wavy legs. Harry remembered he had not given Wolfie any water. He got out of bed and found his flashlight. He got a glass of water and crept down the stairs. The back door squeaked. Harry hoped his parents would not wake up.

Polly heard Harry coming. She turned off her flashlight and held Inky close to her.

Everything looked very different to Harry in the moonlight. The house seemed large, and the trees looked like giants. The doghouse was very dark and silent.

Harry got down on his knees to crawl inside. He pointed his flashlight at the entrance. Two yellow eyes stared at him. Harry remembered how Wolfie had looked under the magnifying glass. He almost stopped breathing. Then Harry heard a noise. It sounded like a giggle. "Wolfie?" he said.

Polly laughed.

"Polly!" cried Harry. "You rat!"

"Did I scare you?" asked Polly.

"No!" said Harry.

"Well," said Polly, "it's very dark out here. Let's go back to the house."

The next morning Polly asked Harry, "Can I see Wolfie today?"

"You have already seen him!" said Harry. "I guess you can."

After breakfast they took the jar of Polly's flies to the doghouse.

"You go first," said Harry.

Polly crawled into the doghouse. "Hello, Wolfie," said Polly.

Harry crawled in after her. Wolfie was in his box, among the leaves.

"He's great, Harry," said Polly.

"Yes," said Harry, "he sure is." He handed Polly the jar of flies. "Here," he said, "you can feed Wolfie today."

Questions

1. Why wouldn't Wolfie spin a web?

2. Harry saw two yellow eyes staring at him. When? Whose eyes did Harry think they were?

3. How do you think Harry felt when he saw the yellow eyes? Why?

4. At first, Harry wouldn't let Polly see Wolfie. What changed his mind?

5. "The *arachnid* held out its *palps* toward me." What does this sentence mean? For whom would it be bad news?

6. Why do you think Miss Rose asked Harry and George so many questions?

Activity   Finish Harry's Report

Harry is writing a report about the ways in which insects and spiders are different. Here are the first two sentences in Harry's report. Copy the sentences. Then finish the report for Harry. Give at least two reasons why spiders are not insects. Use facts from the story to help you.

Spiders Are Not Insects
by Harry

A spider is not an insect. Here are two reasons why.

Spiders Are Special

Spiders That Spin Webs

This web was made by a small garden spider. It is an *orb web* that is shaped like a wheel with many spokes. A web like this might be three feet across. Yet a small spider spun it in about an hour.

Sticky silk threads go around this web. Insects stick to them and are caught. The spider is careful to walk only on the dry, straight threads that go to the web's center. As it moves, the spider keeps coating its legs with oil. Then, if it touches a sticky thread, the spider does not get stuck.

Pictures by Joanna Adamska Koperska

The zigzag marks on the orb web are made of another kind of thread. They are made of thick, fuzzy silk. People have long wondered about these zigzag marks. Some scientists now believe that the zigzags act as a signal to birds. A web is hard to see, but birds can spot the zigzag marks when they fly. When they see the marks, the birds turn away. They do not fly into the web and tear it.

Spiders that spin webs do not see very well. They use webs to trap their food. Some spiders wait in their webs until an insect is trapped. When they feel the web move, they hurry out to get their meal. Other spiders stay in a hiding place. They spin a long thread out to the web. The thread is called a *dragline*. When the dragline moves, the spider knows an insect has been trapped.

Spiders That Hunt

Not all spiders spin webs to catch food. Some spiders are hunters. The jumping spider and the wolf spider both hunt their food.

Spiders that hunt have large eyes. They see much better than spiders that spin. Hunters see well enough to hunt for food. Just below the hunters' eyes are two strong, pointed teeth called *fangs*. Hunting spiders use their fangs to bite and kill insects.

Hunting spiders' bodies are often very hairy. Their legs are thick and powerful. Hunters use their legs in different ways to help them hunt for food. Jumping spiders jump on insects. Wolf spiders run fast enough to catch their food. Some hunting spiders just reach out and grab the insects they want to eat.

jumping
spider

Spiders Everywhere!

Hunting and web-spinning spiders catch and eat millions of insects every year, so spiders live almost anywhere insects live. Spiders live in people's houses. Spiders live in fields and forests. They live in wet basements and dusty barns. They live in caves and swamps, and even underwater. Spiders live everywhere! Look for them. You may find some as small as this dot (•) or as big as this page. You may also find out for yourself what makes spiders so special.

This **crab spider,** a hunter, can change color. It turns pink, white, or yellow so it can't be seen hiding in flowers or leaves.

The **fishing spider** is a hunter that catches and eats small fish.

The **water spider** makes a bell-shaped web that holds a bubble of air. The spider lives, eats, and raises its young in the air bell.

Baby spiders sometimes travel through the air on silk threads.

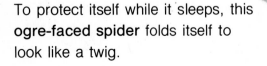

To protect itself while it sleeps, this **ogre-faced spider** folds itself to look like a twig.

The **ray spider** builds a special web that is pulled into an umbrella shape by one thread. When an insect flies in, the thread breaks. The web tangles around the spider's next meal.

Questions

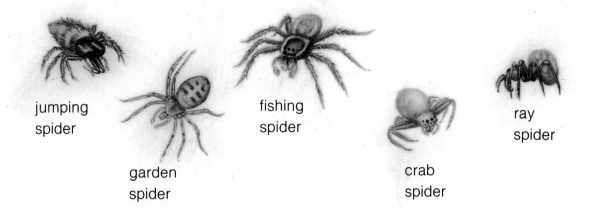

jumping
spider

garden
spider

fishing
spider

crab
spider

ray
spider

1. Which of these spiders are hunters?

2. Which of these spiders spin webs in which to catch their food?

3. What are the three kinds of threads that some garden spiders spin to build their orb webs?

Activity   Design and Label a Web

Design a web you would build if you were a web spinner. Write the name of your web at the top of your paper. Label the different kinds of threads in your web. Then write about how you would use your web to catch insects.

sheet web

cobweb

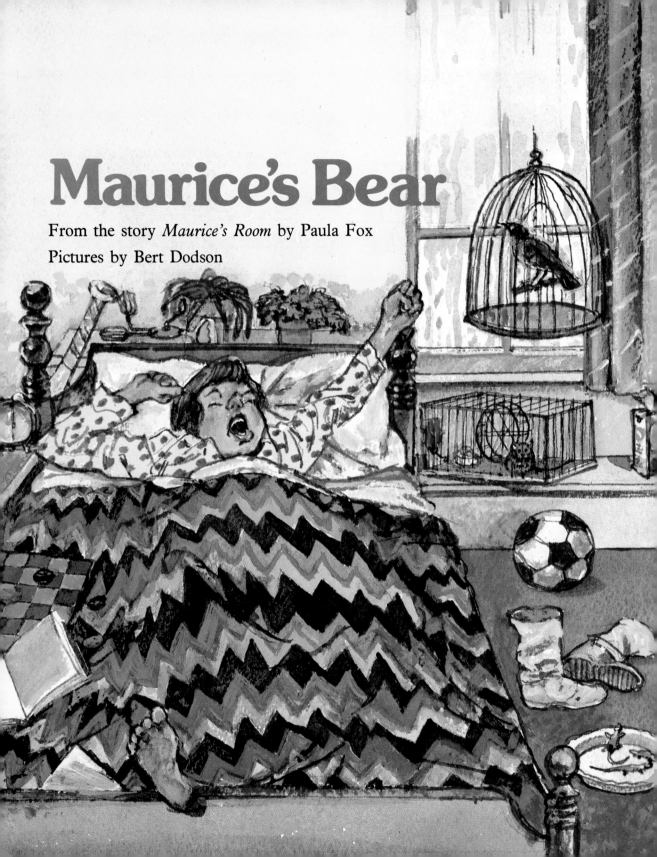

Maurice's Bear

From the story *Maurice's Room* by Paula Fox

Pictures by Bert Dodson

Dead beetles, scraps of wood, a plate of worms, salamanders—these are just some of the things that Maurice keeps in his small room. Maurice is proud of his collection. Unfortunately, his parents don't enjoy it as much as he does. Maurice found most of the things on his own, and his friend Jacob gave him the rest. This morning, Maurice and Jacob are going to pick up a large, stuffed bear that Mr. Klenk, the building janitor, has stored in the basement of their apartment building.

One Saturday morning, Maurice awoke at six o'clock. His window was blurred because it was raining so hard. The hamster stirred in its cage.

"You're up too early," Maurice said. The robin lifted one wing slowly and opened its good eye. Maurice went into the kitchen and made himself a sandwich. It felt good to be eating a sandwich and walking down the hall so early in the morning. No one else was awake. He gave a piece of bread crust to the robin and one to the hamster. Then he got dressed.

Soon there was a soft knock on the front
door. It was Jacob, who always arrived early on
Saturday mornings and who usually brought
something with him. Today he was carrying a
paper sack.

"Do you want a sandwich?" asked Maurice.
Jacob nodded. Then he showed Maurice what he
had brought in the bag.

"What is it?" asked Maurice.

"I think it's for weighing things. I found it in
a box on the street," Jacob said, holding up a
large white scale. The paint was chipped, and
when Maurice pressed his hand down on the
platform, the needle on the dial jiggled.

"Your arm weighs six pounds," said Jacob.

Maurice's mother walked by. She was yawning. She glanced into the room. "Good morning, children," she said.

"My arm is very heavy," said Maurice.

"That's nice," said Maurice's mother, and yawned again and walked on.

"I forgot to tell you," Jacob said. "Mr. Klenk said to come and get the bear."

Maurice put the scale on his bed. Then both boys ran to the front door and down the five flights of stairs to Mr. Klenk's room in the basement. Mr. Klenk was blowing on the cup of coffee he was holding in one hand. He carried a broom in the other.

"It seems I hardly have time for coffee," said Mr. Klenk. "I'll be glad to get rid of that bear."

He left them standing at the door, peering
into his room. In a minute he was back, pushing
the bear before him. The bear's feet were
strapped into roller skates. It was as tall as Jacob.

"Here he is," said Mr. Klenk. "Think you
can handle him?"

Jacob and Maurice stared. The bear was
plump. Its fur was black. Its two front paws
stuck out straight in front of it. The claws were
of different lengths, and some of them pointed
upward as though the bear had been pushing
against a wall.

"Why is it wearing skates?" asked Maurice.

"It came that way," said Mr. Klenk.

"It looks tired," said Jacob.

"It had a long sea voyage, all the way from
South America."

Maurice pulled and Jacob pushed and they got the bear up the stairs all the way to Maurice's front door and inside. Because of the skates the bear moved easily on a level surface, but it had been a slippery business getting it up the stairs.

"I think we'd better wait a while before we show it to my mother and father," said Maurice. "They don't like surprises."

"Mine neither," Jacob said.

Maurice said, "Why don't you get your hat and coat and put them on the bear and maybe they'll think it's you if we push him down the hall fast."

Jacob went to get his outdoor clothes. They dressed the bear, pulling Jacob's hat almost all the way down its muzzle. Then, running, they pushed it down the hall. As they went by his parents' bedroom, Maurice's father poked his head around the door.

"Who's that?" asked Mr. Henry in a sleepy voice.

"Jacob!" said Maurice.

"Maurice!" said Jacob.

Mr. Henry went back to bed. "You shouldn't roller-skate in the house," he said.

At last they got the bear into a corner of Maurice's room. "The bear has a funny smell," said Jacob.

"You're right," said Maurice. "But we'll have to get used to it."

They took Jacob's clothes off the bear. Then they stood and looked at it. It was pleasant to have a big animal in the room with them, even if it was stuffed.

"Maurice," Mrs. Henry called. "Come and drink your apple juice."

"We'll have to disguise it. Then one day when they're feeling good I'll just tell them I have a bear," said Maurice in a whisper. Then he called out, "We'll be there in a minute."

"Couldn't we hide it under the bed for a while?" asked Jacob.

"No," said Maurice. "It won't fit because the Victrola's there. But wait a minute." Maurice opened his closet door and pulled out a heap of clothing. Pretty soon he found what he wanted. It was a penguin costume.

"It was for Halloween," said Maurice.

They started dressing the bear. They had to cut holes in the feet to fit the costume over the bear's roller skates. Then they zipped up the front and pushed the bear between the table and the window. Nothing was left showing of it except the big bumps where its paws were. Then they went to the kitchen and had apple juice and doughnuts.

The next day, which was Sunday, Maurice's uncle was coming to visit. When Maurice heard that his uncle's big dog, Patsy, was coming with him, he went to his room and began to pile up things behind his door.

Maurice's father knocked, and Maurice opened the door a crack.

"Maurice," he said, "you'll have to clean out the hamster's cage. There's a very strong smell coming from your room."

"All right," said Maurice. "I'll do it right now." He looked at the bear in its penguin costume. "I wonder if I could spray you with perfume," he said.

Then he took a piece of rope and tied one
end of it around the bear's neck and the other to
his bedpost. If somebody came in, he decided, he
would just roll the bear out the window and then
pull it back into the room when the coast was clear.

A few minutes later, he heard his mother let his uncle in at the front door.

"Well, Lily, how are you?"

"Fine, and you?"

"Fine, and your husband?"

"Fine, and Patsy?"

"Fine."

"Fine," said Maurice to the hamster.

"And how is Maurice?" asked the uncle.

"Fine," said his mother.

"He'll be delighted to see Patsy."

"He surely will be delighted."

Maurice added his boots to the heap behind his door.

A large object suddenly hurtled down the hall and against Maurice's door. It was Patsy. The barricade gave way, and Patsy raced into the room, stomping and huffing and panting. The snake slid under its rock, the lizard froze, the hamster burrowed in its sawdust, and the bird closed its good eye.

Patsy stopped dead in her tracks. Maurice stood up slowly from where he had been crouching near his bed. Patsy's nose was in the air. She was sniffing. She slid one floppy paw forward, then another. Maurice sprang toward the bear, his arms outstretched.

"Don't lay a hand on that bear!" he cried.

It was too late. Patsy leaped. Over and down crashed the bear. All eight wheels of the roller skates spun in the air. Patsy sat on the bear and began to bay. Maurice could hear his mother, his father, and his uncle racing down the hall.

He ran to the window and flung it open. He grabbed a blanket from his bed and threw it over Patsy, who fell into a tangled heap alongside the bear. In a flash, Maurice had the bear up on its skates and on the sill. He gave it a shove and out it went through the window, the rope trailing behind it.

Mr. Klenk, who was sweeping the courtyard below and whistling softly to himself, heard the whir of spinning roller skates and looked up.

"Good grief!" he cried. "A giant penguin!"

"Whew!" said Maurice. "Safe this time." Then he sank to the floor and smiled.

You can read more about Maurice and his collection in the book, Maurice's Room.

Questions

1. Why did Mr. Klenk think that he saw a giant penguin?

2. If Patsy could talk, what would she say about her visit to Maurice's room?

3. "Patsy sat on the bear and began to *bay*." What does *bay* mean in that sentence?
   a. water with land on three sides
   b. to bark or cry with a deep, long sound
   c. to sniff something

4. Which happening in this story would be the funniest one to *see*? Why do you think so?

5. Why do you think Maurice had so many different kinds of things in his room?

Activity   Write a List

List six unusual things that you might find in Maurice's room. List things that are not in the story. For three of the things, write a sentence telling how or where Maurice got it for his collection.

BOOKSHELF

Tuttle's Shell by Sal Murdocca. Lothrop, Lee & Shepard, 1976. Tuttle the Turtle has lost his shell! He and his friends begin a search to find it.

Miss Nelson Is Missing by Harry Allard and James Marshall. Houghton Mifflin, 1977. The children in Miss Nelson's class misbehave, and their teacher doesn't know what to do. Then one day a substitute teacher comes, and the children wish they had Miss Nelson back.

Warton and Morton by Russell E. Erickson. Lothrop, Lee & Shepard, 1976. Warton, a toad, and his brother Morton go camping, but are separated during a flood.

Oh, What Nonsense! Collected by William Cole. Methuen, 1966. Here are fifty silly poems to make you smile and giggle.

Impossible, Possum by Ellen Conford. Little, Brown, 1971. Randolph has great trouble trying to hang by his tail. The fun begins when his sister Geraldine tricks him into hanging upside down.

2 Helping Hands

Mississippi

Possum

A story by Miska Miles
Pictures by Larry Frederick

Near the Mississippi River, a little gray possum lived in a hollow log.

When he was afraid, which was much of the time, he crept into the log and waited there.

He was afraid of many things. He was afraid of hawks and owls, of bobcats and foxes. And he was afraid of people.

When people came near, he ran into the log and was as still as he knew how to be.

There were things he was not afraid of. He was not afraid of mice or snakes, birds' eggs or berries. These, he ate.

Now, for a long time the rain had fallen and the river water rose and spread out farther along the banks. The possum looked around for food, for he had found nothing to eat for a day.

He looked up into a tree that grew beside the river, and he knew there was a bird's nest high in the branches.

He climbed up above the nest, and held a branch with his back foot, and swung by his tail to look into the nest. The nest was empty.

He climbed down again, and he looked around for berries. While he was looking he felt the earth tremble with footsteps, and he knew that something was coming down the hill, and he was afraid. He ran into his hollow log and was as still as a wild animal can be.

Jefferson Jackson and his sister Rose Mary came down the hill to look at the river.

"Look at that old Mississippi," Jefferson said. "It's getting higher and higher."

For a minute they watched. "It's coming this way," Rose Mary said. She pointed to a little stick lying on the ground. "Watch. The water's touching it." They waited.

"And now the stick's floating off," Jefferson said. "River's coming. Let's tell Papa."

They ran, pounding their feet hard against the ground.

When everything was quiet, the possum came out from his log. The brown river water was creeping along the ground toward him. Now a leaf held it back, then on it came, pushing its slow way—

He turned to go up the hill.

He traveled a long time and he came to a little brown house. He hurried past, for he knew that people lived there.

In this house, Jefferson and Rose Mary were talking to their mother and father.

"We could see the river coming higher while we watched," Jefferson said.

"Right up the hill," said Rose Mary.

"We know," said their mother. "We were about to look for you. We're going up to higher ground, where it's safe."

Quickly she reached for a basket and packed it with corn bread and a cherry pie and a handful of berries.

"The news came over the radio," their father said. "Everybody has to get out. The river's so high that it's breaking through the levee. If it breaks in many more places, it could flood right over this land. Hurry."

"Will we come back?" Rose Mary asked.

"We'll be back when the river goes down," her father said.

"That old river will pour a lot of water into the Gulf," Jefferson said. "Then everything will be just as it's always been."

Now, all this time the possum was trudging up the hill, and he saw many things.

He saw a rabbit and a dog traveling along together and the dog didn't chase the rabbit. He saw a fox and a wild turkey and the fox didn't kill the turkey.

And behind him he heard the river, and he knew he must run from it.

He heard something coming close behind him. Something else was running from the river.

There was no tree he could climb and
the grasses were not thick enough for
hiding. He lay down on the ground and he
didn't move.

Rose Mary and Jefferson and their
mother and father came up the hill.

"Look at the poor little old dead
possum," Rose Mary said.

When everything was still, the possum
slowly got to his feet and looked around.
The river was crowding up the slope of the
hill. A log floated past—maybe his own
log. A boat went by and it was full of
people. He saw a table floating on the
water.

Far ahead were people on their way to the top of the hill, and some drove cows before them, and others led horses—

At the top of the hill, a soldier spoke to Mr. Jackson. "We have a tent for you," he said. "And there's plenty of hot food ready. Before long you'll be home again."

Rose Mary and Jefferson and their parents stood in line for food and for warm gray blankets. And afterward, they went into their tent and lay down on the earth to sleep.

"Wrapped in that blanket, you look like a gray log," Jefferson said.

But Rose Mary didn't hear, for she was asleep.

Night came, and the possum felt his way through the grasses with his whiskers. When he finally reached the top of the dark hill, he was hungry and tired. He looked in the first tent, and he thought he saw four gray logs lying on the ground.

He sniffed the nearest. He smelled an enemy.

Rose Mary sat up. "Papa," she said. "Papa. I heard something."

Her father snapped on a flashlight. "I don't see anything," he said.

"There's another little dead possum," she said.

"Maybe it's not dead," Jefferson said. "Maybe it's only pretending. They do, you know."

"He's an ugly fellow," her father said.

"I think he's nice-looking, for a possum," Rose Mary said. She sat down beside him and touched his rough fur. "He feels cold. He feels dead."

"Put something to eat in front of his nose and see what happens," Jefferson said.

"There are some berries in the basket," his mother said.

Rose Mary put the berries on the ground close to the possum's pointed nose.

The possum lay for a long time as though he were dead, and he hardly dared breathe, he was so frightened. Then he smelled something so good that he had to get up and look around.

The people didn't move and he was very hungry.

He ate the berries. They were fat and
ripe and good. And when he had finished,
the father reached out his hand, and the
possum was afraid. He knew he had to
climb high to be safe. He ran up along
Rose Mary's arm, and she didn't move. He
sat on her shoulder.

This was better than a tree. He was
warm and comfortable. It was almost as
good as a hollow log.

"He's getting tame," Rose Mary said.
"When we go home, we can take him with
us."

And during the days that passed while they waited to go home, planes flew overhead and looked for people and animals who needed help.

Steamboats churned the yellow water and pulled barges loaded with people and animals who had been rescued from the roofs of houses and barns.

Levees were built and made strong to hold the great river. And as the time passed, the possum grew tamer. He followed Rose Mary everywhere.

After a while, the river was caught behind the new levees, and it was time for everyone to go back home.

Jefferson and his mother and father and sister started down the hill, and the possum sat on Rose Mary's shoulder all the way to the little brown house near the bottom of the hill.

Then they were home, and there was a mark high on the wall to show that the Mississippi River had risen almost to the ceiling.

The possum found a hollow log near the back door to live in. Sometimes he came out and sat on Rose Mary's shoulder. More often he hunted for mushrooms or mice, and he wasn't afraid—much of the time.

Questions

1. On the first page of the story, the possum had a problem. What was it?

2. Why did Rose Mary think the possum was dead? How did she find out?

3. Be the possum. What was the most important thing you learned about people in the story?

4. Be Rose Mary. What was the most important thing you learned about possums?

5. What is a *levee*? How does a *levee* help control a river?

Activity   Plan a Story Setting

Every story has a *setting,* the time and place where the story happens. The setting for this story is the Mississippi River and along its banks in the early spring. Suppose you are planning a story about a wild animal. What will be the setting for your story? Draw it. Then list words that will help you tell about that time and place.

The Story of a River

This is the story of a river and its people. The river could be any river, for all rivers have almost the same story. The story begins like this.

Long, long ago in the land that became America, the river began. There were no people in the land then. The young river rushed through the land. It cut through mountains. It carved deep, V-shaped valleys. It shaped the land for the people who would live there someday.

As time passed, the river cut wider valleys. The river spread out and flowed more slowly. The water was deep enough for the big boats that would someday travel on the river.

American Indians were the first people to use the river. To the Indians, the river meant life. It gave them water to drink. It was a place where food could be found—fish, turtles, and wild ducks and geese. The river also gave the Indians a fast way to travel.

Indians lived along the river before Columbus came to America. Some Indians used river clay in building their homes. Others dug ditches that carried river water to their fields. They planted corn, beans, and seeds of other crops in the rich soil of the river valleys.

Pictures by Bob Baumgartner and Joanna Adamska Koperska

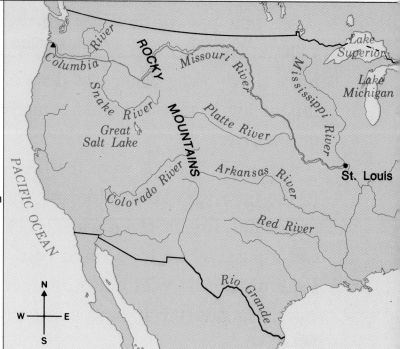

RIVER ROUTE TAKEN BY EXPLORERS LEWIS AND CLARK

MAP KEY

_____ Lewis and Clark's route to the Pacific Ocean

● Trip begins at St. Louis in May 1804

▲ Trip ends at the Pacific Ocean in November 1805

Years passed, and explorers came to America. For some explorers, the river was a highway. Its waters carried them to new lands.

Settlers followed the explorers. They came to America to make new homes. The settlers, too, came to the river. They built their homes on its banks. The river gave them water and food. Then, too, the river was beautiful. It was like a picture that was always moving and changing.

People built farms in the river's wide valleys. When the river flooded, it left rich soil on the land. The farmers did not want their farms to be flooded. Yet they knew their crops would grow well in the valleys' rich soil. So the farmers stayed in the valleys and planted their crops there, year after year.

Loggers came to the tall forests that grew on the river banks. The loggers cut down the trees and floated the logs down the river. Sawmills down the river cut the logs into boards.

More and more people came to America. The river towns grew. Where the river empties into the sea, a town became a mighty city. Today the city is a port with a deep, safe harbor. Ships from all over the world land there. They unload their goods. They take on products made in the river towns and grain grown on the farms far upriver. Then the ships carry their cargo to other places.

Many people depend on the river. They drink river water that has been treated to make it clean. They use products brought by boat up the river. They eat foods grown on the river's banks. Dams along the river produce power that lights people's homes.

The people enjoy the river, too. They admire its beauty. They enjoy swimming, fishing, and boating on the river.

Now the river is old, but its story goes on. The river is still changing. Some parts are getting deeper. In places, its path is changing. The river may one day be even slower and more shallow than it is now. Or, if the earth shifts, the river may become swifter and deeper than before. Yet no matter how the river changes, one thing will stay the same. People will use the river, and enjoy it, and become part of the story it tells.

Questions

1. What are some ways in which the Indians used the river?

2. How did the explorers use the river?

3. Why did towns grow up by the river?

4. How do people today use the river?

Activities

1. **Find Rivers on the Map**

    Look at a map of the United States. Find and list at least three large rivers. After each river, write the name of a large city on that river. Write the names of the states through which the river flows.

2. **Write About River Travel in the Future**

    What will river travel be like in the future? Think about it and then draw a picture of a river boat of the future. Write the name of your boat and some facts about it: how big it is, what makes it move, what it will be used for, and any other details you wish to add.

From

Old Arthur

A story by Liesel Moak Skorpen

Pictures by Diane de Groat

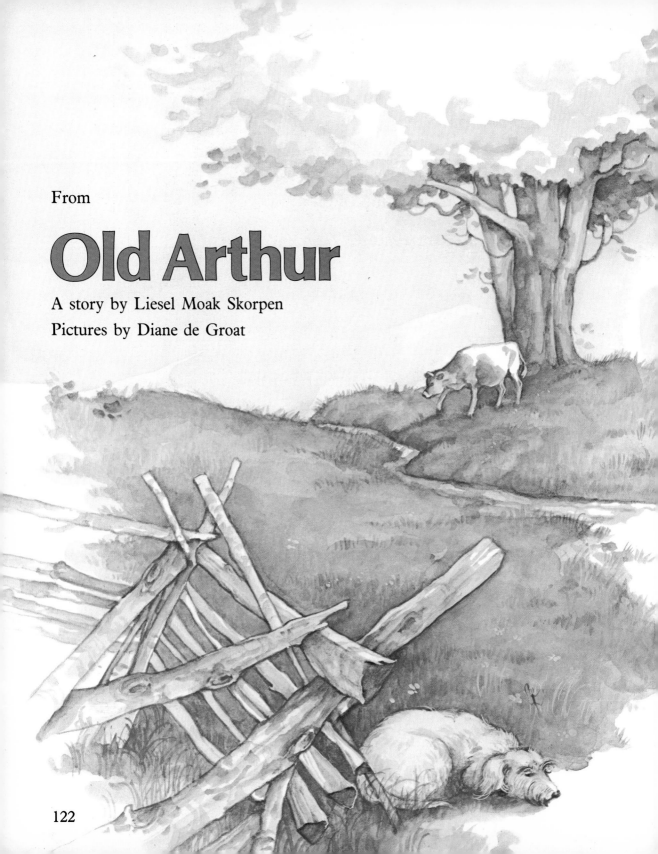

For a long time Old Arthur worked on a farm. He brought the cows home from the fields and kept the fox from the hen house. The day came, however, when Old Arthur was too tired and too sleepy to do his jobs. The farmer thought it was time to get rid of Old Arthur. The old dog knew how the farmer felt so he ran away to town. There the dogcatcher found him and put him in the animal shelter.

Most of the dogs in the animal shelter barked
when anyone opened the door.
But Old Arthur lay on the cold floor of his cage,
closed his old eyes,
and tried to go to sleep.
Sometimes someone stopped beside his cage,
shook his head slowly,
and walked away.
"People want puppies," the dogcatcher said.
"Nobody wants a mangy old mutt like that."

124

A little boy was standing by the cage.
He stood for a long time looking at Old Arthur,
pressing his face against the wire fence.
He didn't shake his head slowly.
He didn't walk away.
"Come here, William," his mother called.
"The puppies are over here."
"I don't want a puppy," William said.

The dogcatcher put his hand on William's shoulder.

"That dog is awful old," he said.

"He's not any good to anyone anymore.
Mind your mother,
and pick out one of the puppies."

"I don't want a puppy," William said.

"This is the one I want.
I like the way he looks at me.
I like the way he almost wags his tail."

William and his mother took Old Arthur home.

The first thing Old Arthur had
was a nice, warm bath.
Arthur had never had a bath before.
The soapsuds worried him a little,
but he was too tired to worry for long.
He closed his old eyes and fell fast asleep
while William was rubbing his back.

The next thing Arthur had
was a nice, warm supper
of milk and buttered toast.
William gave Old Arthur a bowl
with his name on the front
and his picture on the back.

William made a bed for Old Arthur
and put it beside his bed.
He lined the box with a clean, old quilt
to make it soft and warm.
That old dog had never slept in a bed before.
He had never even slept inside a house.
He felt a little lonely in his bed.
He tried to climb on William's bed,
but his legs were too old for jumping.
So William got down behind him
and gave him a little boost.

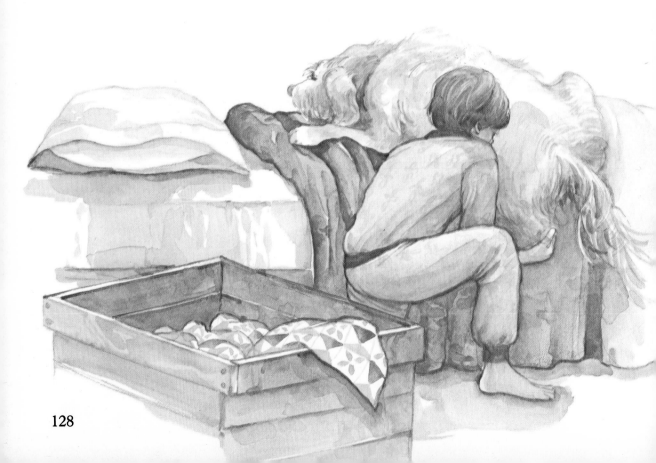

It was Old Arthur's job to wait for William
while William was at school.
That old dog was very good at waiting.
He had waited all his life.

It was Old Arthur's job to go for walks with William.
Nice, slow walks.
They took their time.
They didn't care about fast or far,
and they sat down a lot.
That old dog was good at sitting down.

It was Old Arthur's job to be "it"
for hide-and-seek.
William would hide in his closet
or under his bed.
Old Arthur didn't hunt very fast,
but he hunted very well.
Sometimes William made noises to help.
When Old Arthur found where William was hiding,
he licked him all over his face.

It was Old Arthur's job to lie on his back
while William rubbed his tum.
Old Arthur would wag his woolly tail
and make nice noises that William said were songs.

Wagging that woolly tail was the most important job
that that old dog did.
He wagged it for the baby
who lived in the crib upstairs.
He wagged it for the kittens
who lived in a box out back.
And he wagged it for the soft, gray rabbit
who lived in a wire hutch behind the house.

But his best wags were for William.

"What a good, old dog you are," William said.

"You're good for waiting

and walking

and sitting down

and for lying on your back and singing songs.

You're very good for playing hide-and-seek,

but what I like best is the way you wag your tail."

Then William would put his arms around Old Arthur,

and that old dog would wag that woolly tail

as fast as it would wag.

Questions

1. What did William like best about Old Arthur?

2. What do you think Old Arthur liked best about William?

3. Complete each sentence. Use a word from the story that starts with the same letter as each underlined word.

   a. Old Arthur was good for <u>waiting</u> and _____.

   b. A walk doesn't have to be <u>fast</u> or _____.

   c. Old Arthur <u>wagged</u> his _____ tail.

4. If you were giving Old Arthur the medal below, what good words would it say?

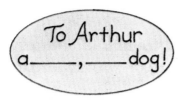

To Arthur
a_____, _____ dog!

Activity   Write About a Pet

If you could have any pet in an animal shelter, what would you choose? Draw the animal's picture. Then write about it. Tell why you would choose this animal for a pet and what you might name it. What would you do to make your pet happy? What could it do to make *you* happy?

Learn About

Illustrators and Illustrations

When you choose a book, do you read the words or look at the pictures first? Many people like to turn the pages and look at the pictures. If they like the pictures, they may be interested in reading the words.

In a picture book the pictures help to tell the story. They show you how the people and the places look, and what is happening. The pictures also show the story's feeling, or *mood.* The pictures tell you if a story is funny, frightening, or sad. Pictures may help you catch the feeling of poems, too.

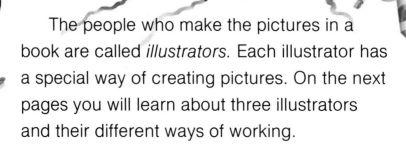

The people who make the pictures in a book are called *illustrators.* Each illustrator has a special way of creating pictures. On the next pages you will learn about three illustrators and their different ways of working.

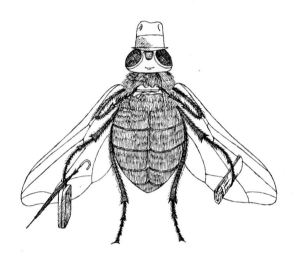

From the poem "The Fly in Rye"
by N. M. Bodecker

    N. M. Bodecker likes to illustrate his
poems with unusual drawings. His poems make
you laugh, and his drawings—a fly, a cherry,
or a pickle dressed in clothing—are funny to see.
    N. M. Bodecker's drawings show that
lines can do many things. See what thin lines
he used to show how light the fly's wings are.
Look at the short, thin lines he used to draw
the fly's fuzzy body and legs. For its eyes, he
used *crosshatching.* He made a set of lines
and then crossed them with another set.

From the story *Stevie*
by John Steptoe

The bold, heavy lines in this picture should catch your attention. Follow the lines around the picture. See how the lines form a circle that brings the mother and her son close together. John Steptoe, the author and illustrator, wants you to feel the love between mother and son. The picture, rather than the words, tells how they feel.

Notice how the bright colors in this picture may *overlap,* or flow one over the other. Look for the overlapping colors on the table.

This illustration was cut from a single piece of paper. Illustrations made this way are called *paper cuts.* Ed Young used this Chinese art form to illustrate *The Emperor and the Kite.* Paper cuts are made with tools that press straight down onto the paper to cut the shapes. Drops of dye are put on the paper to make the blended colors.

In this picture Ed Young helps you feel the excitement of the emperor climbing the rope. The emperor's robes fly out like wings. Imagine how hard it was to cut the emperor's robes.

From the Chinese folk tale *The Emperor and the Kite* retold by Jane Yolen

Now choose a story and illustrate your favorite part. Will you use crayon, paint, or cut paper? Try to catch the story's mood in your picture.

Amelia's Roller Coaster

From the story *Amelia's Flying Machine* by Barbara Shook Hazen

Pictures by Bert Dodson

A wonderful promise had been made to Amelia. Her father had promised to take her to the Chicago Fair for a roller coaster ride. She had to behave herself, though, and follow Grandma Otis's rules while her parents were away. Amelia was so excited about the roller coaster ride that she got her cousins, Katherine and Lucy, and her sister, Muriel, to help her build their own roller coaster. They constructed a wooden track leading from the barn window to the ground. They planned to come down the track in an orange crate fitted with roller skate wheels.

Trial Run

The next day, the roller coaster was ready to try out. Jimmy Watson, who lived on the neighboring farm, came over on his bike. He rode by the barn just as the girls were setting up the roller coaster.

"Not bad," said Jimmy when he saw it. "Not bad at all. But does it work? That's what I want to see."

"You will," said Amelia. "Just wait."

Jimmy leaned his bike against a tree. He sat down on the grass and watched. "Who's going to go first?" he asked.

"We could draw straws," said Amelia. "That would be fairest."

"No thanks," said Katherine. "Not me. You go first, Amelia."

"Yes, you first," said Lucy. "It was all your idea."

Muriel looked up at the track slanting out of the hayloft window and shuddered. "Not me, Meeley," she said. "It looks awfully high."

"See," Jimmy taunted. "Your sister is scared. Your cousins are scared. You're all scared to try it."

"Is that so?" said Amelia. "Well, I'm not scared. I'll gladly go first!"

Amelia tested the track to make sure it was firmly set on the ground. Then she picked up the roller coaster car. She carried it up the ladder to the hayloft and placed it on the wooden track. And then she squeezed herself inside the car. It was a tight fit.

She pushed herself part way out the barn window. She held on tight to the track sides and looked out. It was a long way down.

"What are you waiting for?" Jimmy called. "Are you scared?"

"Nope, not a bit!" said Amelia, letting go of the track sides.

The orange-crate car started to roll. It went faster and faster down the track. Amelia hugged her knees and held on tight. "Whee!" she cried. "I'm flying!"

The car gathered speed as it raced down the track. It hit the ground with a hard bump. It landed so hard that it flipped over.

Amelia flew out and fell on the ground. She lay on her stomach moaning, "Ooooooooooooh!"

Katherine and Lucy and Muriel raced to her.

"Are you hurt?" asked Lucy, trying to see Amelia's face.

Even Jimmy looked worried. He held out a hand to help Amelia up. "Are you okay?" he asked.

"Sure. I'm okay," Amelia gasped. She turned herself over and brushed the dirt off her clothes.

Then she sat up and folded her arms. "I'm okay, all right," she said. "But the track isn't. The track is too short. That makes the slant too steep. And that's why the car hit the ground so hard.

"What we have to do," she said, getting up, "is add more boards and make the track longer."

"Why don't you just call it quits, huh?" suggested Jimmy.

"Not now!" said Amelia. "Not when I know what went wrong." She looked at Jimmy. "Come back this afternoon. You'll see how well it works."

Back to Work

Soon they were at it again. Amelia and Muriel laid the track on the ground. They added more boards until it was twice as long as before.

It was hard work, and it seemed even hotter than the day before. Katherine and Lucy went to the kitchen to make some lemonade.

Amelia ripped her stockings and Muriel got a splinter in her little finger. "Just a little longer," Amelia kept saying. "Just a few more boards."

They were almost done when Katherine and Lucy came back. "I hope Grandma Otis doesn't spoil everything," said Lucy. "She sounded suspicious. She wanted to know what we were up to."

"What did you tell her?" asked Amelia.

"The truth, of course," smiled Lucy. "I told her we were making lemonade and were going to take it out to you. Then I asked her if she wanted some. Then Grandma looked down her glasses and said, 'Young lady, I smell something fishy.' And I said, 'But, Grandma Otis, we haven't been near the river.'"

"And then we got out of there fast," said Katherine. She shook her head, "If Grandma decides to come out here, you're a goner."

"At least my trip to Chicago is," said Amelia.

A Second Try

When the lemonade was gone, the girls all helped to set up the track.

"It looks okay," said Amelia. "Let's just hope it works this time."

Soon Jimmy came back. "I wouldn't miss this for anything," he said with a grin.

Amelia made a face at him. Then she turned to the others. Once more she asked, "Shall we draw straws to see who goes first?"

"Not me," said Katherine. "Not after last time."

"Don't look at me," said Lucy.

Muriel shook her head. "Not me, Meeley," she said. "But if you go, I'll keep my fingers crossed."

"I knew it," said Jimmy. "You're too scared!"

Amelia stamped her foot. "That's not so," she said. "I'm not scared. Just you watch."

She climbed up to the hayloft and squeezed into the car. There she paused and took a deep breath. "It's got to work," she whispered to herself. "It's just got to."

"What are you waiting for?" teased Jimmy. "Santa Claus? Or me to try it for you?"

"Don't listen to him," yelled Lucy.

"Don't do it," said Katherine under her breath.

Muriel turned her head. She crossed as many fingers as she could. She closed her eyes tight. She didn't want to watch.

But she did want to see what was going on. When she opened her eyes to peek, she looked up and screamed, "Stop, Meeley! You can't go!"

The warning came too late. Amelia had just let go. The car started to roll. As it picked up speed, it went faster and faster down the long track.

Amelia felt the speed and the slap of wind in her face. "Wow! Look at me," she shouted. "I'm really flying!"

The orange crate kept going. It rolled to the end of the track, and then onto the ground. Amelia waved and grinned at Jimmy as she went by, and he grinned back at her.

The car finally came to a stop—right by
a pair of black-stockinged feet.

"Oh-oh," gulped Amelia, looking up.

Grandmother Otis stared down at
Amelia. Her hands were on her hips. Her
eyebrows met in a disapproving *V*.

She spoke in her slow we'll-get-to-the-bottom-of-this voice. "Amelia Mary, what are you up to? And what kind of fool contraption is this? I suspected something. And I suspect your father will have something to say when he hears about it."

Grandmother Otis tapped her foot. "Young lady, was all this your idea?" she asked. "Or did somebody put you up to it?"

Amelia groaned. Telling the truth meant missing Chicago and the Fair and going with her father and everything.

"Yes, Gram," she said in a small voice. "It was all my idea." Then she sighed deeply.

Grandma Otis sighed, too. "Amelia Mary, I daresay I don't know whatever will become of you if you . . . "

"Ma'am," Jimmy interrupted, "it really wasn't Amelia's fault. I mean, she made it and rode on it. But I guess I kind of put her up to it."

Grandmother Otis turned toward Jimmy. She squinted through her glasses. "I might have thought so," she said. "I didn't think any granddaughter of mine could do such a foolhardy thing."

She shook her finger at Jimmy. "Yes, I should have known you were behind this, Jimmy Watson. You have a habit of getting into mischief. Why, I have half a mind . . ."

Amelia jumped to her feet. "No, Grandma! Jimmy's not to blame. I'm the one who . . ."

"I don't want to listen," said Grandma Otis sternly. She picked up her skirts. "Amelia. Muriel. Girls. Come with me," she ordered.

"As for you, young man"—she squinted hard at Jimmy—"you stay right here and take down this contraption. Right now. Break it up, every bit of it, mind you."

She turned on her heels and headed for the house.

Amelia hung back. "It isn't fair," she said to Jimmy. "You're getting the blame. It was my idea."

"So what!" Jimmy shrugged. "She'll get over it, and you'll get to go to Chicago. She never tells my pa, and she won't tell yours either."

"Know something?" Amelia smiled. "You're okay."

Jimmy grinned back. "Just send me a postcard with a picture of the roller coaster on it."

The Real Amelia

Amelia's full name was Amelia Earhart
(EHR•hahrt). She grew up in the early 1900s, a
time when the first airplanes were being flown.
Not only did Amelia learn to fly, but she became
one of the finest pilots of her time.

Amelia Earhart was the first woman to fly across
the Atlantic Ocean alone. She received many honors
for her solo flight, but she wanted to do something
that no pilot had ever done. She wanted to fly
around the world at the equator—a more difficult
and dangerous route than any that had ever been
flown.

In 1937 Amelia Earhart and her co-pilot Fred
Noonan began their flight around the world. They
made stops at South America, Africa, and India.
Then they started across the Pacific Ocean. While
looking for a tiny island in the Pacific where they
were to refuel, they disappeared. They were never
seen again. Nothing of their plane was ever found.

In a letter she left for her husband, Amelia
Earhart had spoken about her flight. She had written,
"I want to do it because I want to do it. Women
must try to do things as men have tried. When they
fail, their failures must be but a challenge to others."

Questions

1. Amelia said something that showed she was enjoying her ride on the roller coaster. What did she say?

2. Muriel screamed, "Stop, Meeley! You can't go!" Why did Muriel say that?

3. In this story, two people were brave in different ways. Who were they? How did they show they were brave?

4. Which sentence below shows the meaning of this sentence: Grandma Otis was suspicious of Amelia's contraption.
   a. Grandma was puzzled by Amelia's actions.
   b. Grandma was angry at Amelia's machine.
   c. Grandma was distrustful of Amelia's strange invention.

Activity   Plan and Draw a Ride

Draw a *diagram,* or plan, for an exciting ride. Show what people would ride on or in. Show where the ride would go. Make sure that the ride would be *safe* so that no one would get hurt. Label each part of your diagram.

BOOKSHELF

Big City Port by Betsy Maestro and Ellen DelVecchio. Four Winds Press, 1983. Colorful ships of all kinds move in and out of a big city's harbor.

Harry's Dog by Barbara Ann Porte. Greenwillow Books, 1984. Harry knows his father couldn't have a dog when he was little because of an allergy, so Harry picks a better present for his father.

His Mother's Dog by Liesel Moak Skorpen. Harper & Row, 1978. A boy who has always wanted a dog is upset when the new puppy comes.

Three Days on a River in a Red Canoe by Vera B. Williams. Greenwillow Books, 1981. Two cousins and their mothers buy a red canoe so they can take a weekend trip along a river.

The 329th Friend by Marjorie Weinman Sharmat. Four Winds Press, 1979. Though Emery Raccoon invited 328 guests to lunch, none of them has time to listen to him.

3 Tell Me the Name

RUMPELSTILTSKIN

A German folk tale retold by Edith H. Tarcov

Pictures by Edward Gorey

PART ONE

Once upon a time there was a poor miller who had a beautiful daughter.

One morning, the king came riding by. He stopped to talk to the miller. The miller wanted to say something interesting. So he said: "King, I have a daughter—"

"I suppose she is beautiful," said the king.

"Oh, yes. She is beautiful," the miller said. "But she is more than that. My daughter . . . MY daughter . . . can spin straw into gold!"

"Spin straw into gold?" said the king. "Hm. Well! Tell your daughter to come to see me."

That evening the miller's daughter came to the king. The king took her into a little room. There was nothing in the room but

> a heap of straw,
>
> a chair,
>
> and a spinning wheel.

"Now spin," said the king. "If you do not spin all this straw into gold by morning, you must die."

The king locked the door and went away.

Now the poor miller's daughter was all alone. She really did not know how to spin straw into gold. She did not know what to do. So she began to cry.

Suddenly the door opened, and a tiny little man came in.

"Good evening, miller's daughter," he said. "Why are you crying?"

"Oh!" she said. "Oh! The king told me to spin all this straw into gold. If it's not done by morning, I must die!"

"What will you give me if I do it for you?" the little man asked.

"I will give you my necklace," said the miller's daughter.

The little man took the necklace. Then he sat down at the spinning wheel.

Whirl! Whirl! Whirl! Three times he whirled
the wheel and the work was done. Now that heap
of straw was a heap of gold. And the little man
went away.

As soon as the sun was up, the king came in.
He looked at the heap of gold. The king was
pleased.

"You have done well," he said to the miller's
daughter. "But I need more gold than that."

That evening the king took the miller's
daughter into a bigger room. There was nothing
in that room but

        a chair,

        a spinning wheel,

        and a great big heap of straw.

"Now spin," said the king. "If you do not
spin all this straw into gold by morning, you
must die."

The king locked the door and went away.

Again the poor miller's daughter was all
alone. She looked at all that straw. She did not
know what to do. So she began to cry.

Again the door opened and the little man
came in.

"Good evening, miller's daughter," he said. "What will you give me if I spin all this straw into gold?"

"I will give you my ring," said the miller's daughter.

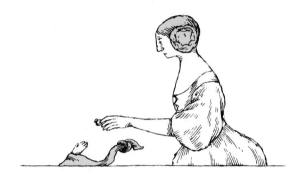

The little man took the ring. Then he sat down at the spinning wheel.

Whirl! Whirl! Whirl! Three times he whirled the wheel and the work was done. Now that great big heap of straw was a great big heap of gold. And the little man went away.

As soon as the sun was up, the king came in. He looked at that great big heap of gold. The king was pleased.

"You have done well," he said to the miller's daughter. "But I need more gold than that."

That evening the king took the miller's daughter into a very big room. There was nothing in that room but

> a chair,
>
> a spinning wheel,
>
> and heaps and heaps of straw!

"Now spin," said the king. "If you spin all this straw into gold by morning, you will be my wife."

The king locked the door and went away.

When the miller's daughter was all alone, the little man came again.

Again he said, "Good evening, miller's daughter. What will you give me if I spin all this straw into gold?"

"I have nothing left to give you," she said.

"Nothing?" the little man asked.

"Nothing," said the miller's daughter.

"I will help you," said the little man. "But you must promise to give me something. . . . "

"Anything! Anything you ask!" she cried.

"Then promise me," the little man said. "Promise me that when you are queen you will give me your first baby."

"Yes! Yes! I promise!" said the miller's daughter. And she thought, Who knows if I really shall be queen? And if I am queen, who knows if I shall have a baby? "Yes! Yes!" she said again. "I promise!"

The little man sat down at the spinning wheel.

Whirl! Whirl! Whirl! Three times he whirled the wheel and the work was done. Now those heaps and heaps of straw were heaps and heaps of gold. And the little man went away.

As soon as the sun was up the king came in. He looked at the heaps and heaps of gold. The king was very pleased.

"My dear," said the king. "We will be married this very day!"

And so the miller's daughter became queen.

A year later, the king and queen had a beautiful baby.

PART TWO

One evening the queen was in her room, playing with her baby. Suddenly, the little man came into the room.

"Good evening, queen," he said. "Now give me what you promised."

The queen had forgotten the little man. She had forgotten her promise, too.

"What promise?" she asked.

"You promised to give me your first baby," said the little man.

"I cannot give you my baby," said the queen. "You may have all the riches of the kingdom, but let me keep my baby."

"No, queen," said the little man. "A baby is dearer to me than all the riches of the world."

The queen began to cry. She cried so hard that the little man felt sorry for her.

"I will give you three days," he said. "If in three days you know my name, you may keep your baby. I will come every evening, for three evenings. Each time I will ask if you know my name."

And the little man went away.

The next morning the queen called for her messenger. "Messenger," she said. "Go through the town. Find out all the names people have. Come back before evening and tell them all to me."

That evening the little man came into the queen's room.

"Good evening, queen," he said. "Do you know my name?"

"Is it Al?" she asked.

"No," said the little man. "That's not my name."

"Is it Bill?"

"No."

"Is it Charlie?"

"No."

So they went, on and on and on. But all the little man said was: "No. No, no. That's not my name."

That very evening, as soon as the little man had gone away, the queen called for her messenger.

"Messenger," she said. "Go through the kingdom. Find out all the strange names people have. Come back tomorrow, before evening, and tell them all to me. Hurry."

On the second evening the little man came into the queen's room.

"Good evening, queen," he said. "Do you know my name?"

The queen asked him all the strange names her messenger had found.

"Is it Angel Face?" she asked.

"No," said the little man. "That's not my name."

"Is it Bump-on-a-Lump?"

"No."

"Is it Diddle Dump?"

"No."

So they went, on and on and on. But all the little man said was: "No. No, no. That's not my name."

That evening, as soon as the little man had gone away, the queen called for her messenger.

"Messenger," she said. "Go once more through the kingdom. You must find more names for me! Come back tomorrow, before evening, and tell them all to me. Hurry!"

On the third day, it was almost evening when the messenger came back.

"I could not find any new names for you," he said.

"Not any new names at all?" asked the queen.

"Well," said the messenger. "I did find something. Something very strange . . . "

"Tell me," said the queen. "And hurry!"

"Last night," he said, "I went up high, high into the mountains. I went deep into the woods. There I saw a little house. In front of that little house there was a fire. And around that little fire a tiny man was dancing. While he was dancing, he was singing:

Tonight my cakes I bake.
Tonight my brew I make.
Tomorrow, tomorrow, tomorrow
The queen's little baby I take!
Lucky I'll go as lucky I came
For RUMPELSTILTSKIN is my name!"

How happy the queen was to hear that name!

Now it was the third evening, and the little man came again.

"Good evening, queen," he said. "Do you know my name?"

"Tell me, is it Tom?" the queen asked.

"No."

"Hm . . . let me see. Is it Dick?"

"No."

"Well, let me think . . . . Is it Harry?"

"No." The little man laughed and he shook his head. "No, no. That's not my name."

"Then . . . tell me . . . " asked the queen. "Could it be . . . ? Is it . . . RUMPELSTILTSKIN?"

How angry the little man was! He stamped so hard with his right foot that he made a deep hole in the floor.

Oh, he was angry! He stamped hard with his left foot, too. And he fell deep into the earth.

No one has seen him since.

Questions

1. The miller's daughter had two big problems. What were they?

2. Which rule fits each person in the story?
   Rumpelstiltskin   King   Daughter   Miller

   a. Don't be greedy.
   b. Don't brag about your children.
   c. Don't make promises you can't keep.
   d. Don't stamp too hard on the floor!

3. What is the only color the artist used in his pictures for this story? Why do you think he used only that color?

4. What work does a *miller* do?
   a. weaves cloth
   b. grinds grain
   c. drives horses

Activity   Write Your Opinion

Draw yourself. Write what you would say about the Queen and what she did in the story.

I don't think the Queen played fair.

She did what she had to do. She didn't want to lose her life or her baby.

I Am Rose

From a poem by Gertrude Stein

I am Rose my eyes are blue
I am Rose and who are you?
I am Rose and when I sing
I am Rose like anything.

Pictures by Susan Jaekel

Pudden Tame

A folk rhyme

What's your name?
　　Pudden Tame.
What's your other?
　　Bread and Butter.
Where do you live?
　　In a sieve.
What's your number?
　　Cucumber.

182

Pudden Tame

A folk rhyme

What's your name?
   Pudden Tame.
What's your other?
   Bread and Butter.
Where do you live?
   In a sieve.
What's your number?
   Cucumber.

From

Rufus M.

A story by Eleanor Estes
Pictures by Susan Lexa

Rufus Moffat wanted a book. His older brother and his sisters were reading library books, but they said he was too young. Besides, he couldn't even read yet. That made Rufus mad. He knew how to get to the library by himself. He even knew where to find one of the Brownie books he liked. Reading? It was easy. Flipping pages. He could do that. It would be just as easy to take a book out of the library. So Rufus went to the library, chose his book, and handed it to the lady behind the desk.

"Do you have a card?" the lady asked.

Rufus felt in his pockets. Sometimes he carried around an old playing card or two. Today he didn't have one.

"No," he said.

"You'll have to have a card to get a book."

"I'll go and get one," said Rufus.

The lady put down her cards. "I mean a library card," she explained kindly. "It looks to me as though you are too little to have a library card. Do you have one?"

"No," said Rufus. "I'd like to though."

"I'm afraid you're too little," said the lady. "You have to write your name to get one. Can you do that?"

Rufus nodded his head confidently. Writing. Lines up and down. He'd seen that done. And the letters that Mama had tied in bundles in the closet under the stairs were covered with writing. Of course he could write.

"Well, let's see your hands," said the lady.

Rufus obligingly showed this lady his hands, but she did not like the look of them. She cringed and clasped her head as though the sight hurt her.

"Oh," she gasped. "You'll just have to go home and wash them before we can even think about joining the library and borrowing books."

This was a complication upon which Rufus had not reckoned. However, all it meant was a slight delay. He'd wash his hands and then he'd get the book. He turned and went out of the library, found his scooter safe among the Christmas trees, and pushed it home. He surprised Mama by asking to have his hands washed. When this was done, he mounted his scooter again and returned all the long way to the library. It was not just a little trip to the library. It was a long one. A long one and a hot one on a day like this. But he didn't notice that. All he was bent on was getting his book and taking it home and reading with the others on the front porch. They were all still there, brushing flies away and reading.

Again Rufus hid his scooter in the pine trees, encircled the light, and went in.

"Hello," he said.

"Well," said the lady. "How are they now?"

Rufus had forgotten he had had to wash his hands. He thought she was referring to the other Moffats. "Fine," he said.

"Let me see them," she said, and she held up her hands.

Oh! His hands! Well, they were all right, thought Rufus, for Mama had just washed them. He showed them to the lady. There was a silence while she studied them. Then she shook her head. She still did not like them.

"Ts, ts, ts!" she said. "They'll have to be cleaner than that."

Rufus looked at his hands. Supposing he went all the way home and washed them again, she still might not like them. However, if that is what she wanted, he would have to do that before he could get the Brownie book . . . and he started for the door.

"Well now, let's see what we can do," said the lady. "I know what," she said. "It's against the rules but perhaps we can wash them in here." And she led Rufus into a little room that smelled of paste where lots of new books and old books were stacked up. In one corner was a little round sink and Rufus washed his hands again. Then they returned to the desk. The lady got a chair and put a newspaper on it. She made Rufus stand on this because he was not big enough to write at the desk otherwise.

Then the lady put a piece of paper covered with a lot of printing in front of Rufus, dipped a pen in the ink well and gave it to him.

"All right," she said. "Here's your application. Write your name here."

All the writing Rufus had ever done before had been on big pieces of brown wrapping paper with lots of room on them. Rufus had often covered those great sheets of paper with his own kind of writing at home. Lines up and down.

But on this paper there wasn't much space. It was already covered with writing. However, there was a tiny little empty space and that was where Rufus must write his name, the lady said. So, little space or not, Rufus confidently grasped the pen with his left hand and dug it into the paper. He was not accustomed to pens, having always worked with pencils until now, and he made a great many holes and blots and scratches.

"Gracious," said the lady. "Don't bear down so hard! And why don't you hold it in your right hand?" she asked, moving the pen back into his right hand.

Rufus started again scraping his lines up and down and all over the page, this time using his right hand. Wherever there was an empty space he wrote. He even wrote over some of the print for good measure. Then he waited for the lady, who had gone off to get a book for some man, to come back and look.

"Oh," she said as she settled herself in her swivel chair, "is that the way you write? Well . . . it's nice, but what does it say?"

"Says Rufus Moffat. My name."

Apparently these lines up and down did not spell Rufus Moffat to this lady. She shook her head.

"It's nice," she repeated. "Very nice. But nobody but you knows what it says. You have to learn to write your name better than that before you can join the library."

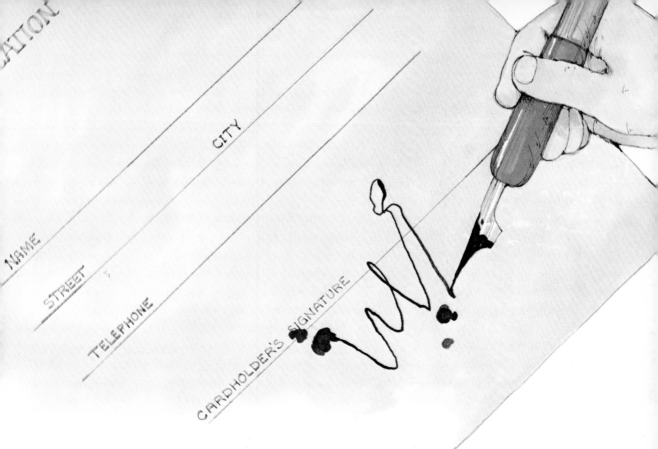

Rufus was silent. He had come to the library all by himself, gone back home to wash his hands, and come back because he wanted to take books home and read them the way the others did. He had worked hard. He did not like to think he might have to go home without a book.

The library lady looked at him a moment and then she said quickly before he could get himself all the way off the big chair, "Maybe you can *print* your name."

Rufus looked at her hopefully. He thought he could write better than he could print, for his writing certainly looked to him exactly like all grown people's writing. Still he'd try to print if that was what she wanted.

The lady printed some letters on the top of a piece of paper. "There," she said. "That's your name. Copy it ten times and then we'll try it on another application."

Rufus worked hard. He worked so hard the knuckles showed white on his brown fist.

He worked for a long, long time, now with his right hand and now with his left. Sometimes a boy or a girl came in, looked over his shoulder and watched, but he paid no attention. From time to time the lady studied his work and she said, "That's fine. That's fine." At last she said, "Well, maybe now we can try." And she gave him another application.

All Rufus could get, with his large generous letters, in that tiny little space where he was supposed to print his name, was R-U-F. The other letters he scattered here and there on the card. The lady did not like this either. She gave him still another blank. Rufus tried to print smaller and this time he got RUFUS in the space, and also he crowded an M at the end. Since he was doing so well now the lady herself printed the *offat* part of Moffat on the next line.

"This will have to do," she said. "Now take this home and ask your mother to sign it on the other side. Bring it back on Thursday and you'll get your card."

Rufus's face was shiny and streaked with
dirt where he had rubbed it. He never knew
there was all this work to getting a book.
The other Moffats just came in and got
books. Well, maybe they had had to do this
once too.

Rufus held his hard-earned application in
one hand and steered his scooter with the
other. When he reached home Joey, Jane
and Sylvie were not around any longer.
Mama signed his card for him, saying, "My!
So you've learned how to write!"

"Print," corrected Rufus.

Mama kissed Rufus and he went back out. The lady had said to come back on Thursday, but he wanted a book today. When the other Moffats came home, he'd be sitting on the top step of the porch, reading. That would surprise them. He smiled to himself as he made his way to the library for the third time.

When he reached home, he showed Mama his book. She smiled at him, and gave his cheek a pat. She thought it was fine that he had gone to the library and joined all by himself and taken out a book. And she thought it was fine when Rufus sat down at the kitchen table, was busy and quiet for a long, long time, and then showed her what he had done.

He had printed RUFUS M. That was what he had done. And that's the way he learned to sign his name. And that's the way he always did sign his name for a long, long time.

Questions

1. What did a *card* mean to Rufus?

2. What did a *card* mean to the librarian?

3. Rufus had several problems in this story. What was one of those problems? How did Rufus solve it?

4. Someone said, "I think Rufus should have waited a year longer before he tried to get a library card." Do you agree? Tell why or why not.

5. If you have a *complication,* you are likely to have a _____.
   a. problem   b. library card   c. surprise

6. If someone gives you an *application,* what do you get?
   a. a book   b. a printed form   c. a list

Activity   Make a Book List

Rufus has a library card now. Make a list of five books you think Rufus would like. Write the author's name after each book title. For each book, tell why you think Rufus would like it.

About ELEANOR ESTES

Though she always wanted to become a writer, Eleanor Estes (EHS•teez) said, "I never really decided to write for children. It just happened that I did." She has filled her warm and funny stories with many memories of her own childhood. Often, in the middle of the night, she would remember what someone said or did. She wrote these memories down, and later used them in the stories she wrote.

Eleanor Estes grew up in West Haven, Connecticut. After graduating from high school, she worked as a librarian. When her first book, *The Moffats,* was published, she decided to become a full-time writer. Several of her books are about the adventures of the Moffat family.

More Books by Eleanor Estes

The Hundred Dresses
The Middle Moffat
Ginger Pye
The Moffat Museum

Paper Boats

A poem by Rabindranath Tagore

Day by day I float my paper boats one by one down
the running stream.
In big black letters I write my name on them and
the name of the village where I live.
I hope that someone in some strange land will
find them and know who I am.
I load my little boats with *shiuli* flowers from
our garden, and hope that these blooms of dawn
will be carried safely to land in the night.
I launch my paper boats and look up into the sky
and see the little clouds setting their white
bulging sails.
I know not what playmate of mine in the sky sends
them down the air to race with my boats!
When night comes I bury my face in my arms and
dream that my paper boats float on and on
under the midnight stars.
The fairies of sleep are sailing in them, and the
lading is their baskets full of dreams.

Picture by Christa Kieffer

The Naming of
Olga da Polga

A story from *The Tales of Olga da Polga* by Michael Bond
Pictures by Mike Muir

Olga da Polga lived in a crowded pet shop with a lot of other guinea pigs. Yet Olga da Polga wasn't like the others. She had a gleam in her eyes, an unusual name, and big dreams about "going places." The other guinea pigs were afraid of the outside world, but Olga could hardly wait to get there.

One day, quite suddenly, Olga da Polga's dreams came true. A man and his daughter came into the shop, bought Olga da Polga, and took her home.

If Olga da Polga's new home wasn't exactly a palace it certainly seemed like it, and it was definitely the nearest she was ever likely to get to one.

After the cramped and crowded conditions in the pet shop it was like entering a different world.

The hutch was large and airy and it was divided into two halves. Both floors were neatly covered with sawdust and the rooms were separated by a wall which had a hole cut in the middle so that she could easily pass between the two.

The first half was a kind of all-purpose room, part dining room, part playroom. The room had a wire mesh door, a small ash branch in one corner so that Olga could keep her teeth nice and sharp, and two heavy bowls—one marked OATS and the other marked WATER.

Olga tried out both before turning her attention to the second room. This turned out to be even more exciting than the first, for it not only had a *glass window* to keep out the weather, but there was a large, inviting mound of fresh-smelling hay as well.

Olga spent some time pressing the hay flat so that she would have somewhere comfortable to sleep without being too hot, and then she settled down to think things over.

Really, all things considered, life had taken a very pleasant turn.

The sun was shining. The birds were chirping. Even the noises seemed friendly. Olga enjoyed the clinkings, singing,

and occasional humming sounds from somewhere inside the big house as Mr. and Mrs. Sawdust—which was what Olga had decided to call them—went about their work.

Every so often there was a reassuring murmur of voices outside as one or other of the family peered through the glass to make certain she was all right.

First came Mr. Sawdust, then Mrs. Sawdust, then some other people called "neighbors" and they all had a friendly word or two to say to her.

Finally Karen Sawdust herself arrived with an enormous pile of grass, a bunch of dandelions, and a large juicy carrot neatly sliced down the center, which she placed temptingly alongside the feeding bowl.

"We're going to choose a name for you now," Karen announced, as Olga stirred herself and came out of the bedroom to sample these new delicacies. "And we have to make sure it's right because tomorrow Daddy's going to paint it over your front door. There'll be no changing it once that's done."

Olga nibbled away, half listening, half in a world of her own.

"Daddy fancies Greta and Mummy's rather keen on Gerda, but I'm not sure. They don't sound *special* enough to me." Karen Sawdust put her face against the door as she turned to go. "I do wish you could tell us what *you* would like for a name."

"Greta? . . . Gerda? . . . *Painted on my front door?*" Olga's world suddenly turned upside down.

She paused, a carefully folded piece of grass half in, half out of her mouth, hardly able to believe her ears.

"But I'm Olga da Polga," she wailed, addressing the empty air. "I've always been Olga da Polga. I can't change now—I really can't." That night, long after darkness fell and everyone else had gone to bed, Olga was still wide awake and deep in thought.

"I suppose," she said to herself, for what seemed like the hundredth time, "I suppose I ought to be counting my blessings instead of grumbling. I mean . . . I have a nice new home . . . food . . . I'm among friends . . . but I *would* like to keep my own name, especially as I'm having it painted on."

The more Olga thought about it the sadder she became, for she couldn't help remembering a remark one of the older inhabitants of the pet shop had once made. "Always hang on to your name," he had said. "It may not be much, but when you're a guinea pig it's sometimes all you have in the world."

Olga's own name was firmly imprinted on her mind. OLGA DA POLGA.

It had taken her fancy straight away and now she had become so used to it she couldn't begin to picture having anything else. When she closed her eyes she could still see it written in large block letters on the side of an old cardboard box.

Suddenly she jumped up in excitement, her mind in a whirl. Could she? Was it possible?

It would mean a lot of hard work. A lot of difficult, almost impossible work. And yet . . .

Getting out of her warm bed, shivering partly with the chill of the night air and partly with she knew not what, Olga made her way through into the next room.

Clutching the ash branch firmly in her mouth she set to work. Scratching and scraping, starting and stopping, she worked and she worked and she worked. Sometimes pausing to smooth the sawdust over before beginning all over again, she tried not once, but time after time and still it wouldn't come right.

Dawn was breaking before she crawled
back into her bedroom at long last and
sank down in the hay. Her paws were
aching, her fur was covered in sawdust, and
her eyes were so tired she could hardly
bear to keep them open.

"It looks plain enough to me," she thought, gazing back at the result of her night's work, "but then, I *know* what it's meant to be. I only hope the others understand as well."

Gradually, as she enjoyed her well-earned rest, the air began to fill with sounds of morning. They were strange, unaccustomed sounds. In place of the usual grunts and rustles of the pet shop there were dogs barking, clocks striking, the sound of bottles clinking, and somewhere in the distance the noise of a train rattling on its way. In fact, there were so many different noises Olga soon lost count of them.

And then, at long last, came the one she had been waiting for. There was a click, the clatter of a bolt being withdrawn, and a moment later a now familiar face appeared on the other side of the wire netting.

In the pause which followed, Olga could almost hear the beating of her own heart.

"Mummy! Mummy!" With a shriek of surprise the face vanished from view. "Come quickly! Come and see!"

Olga jumped to her feet. "Wheeee! It's worked! It's worked! Wheeeeeee!" Squeaking with joy and pleasure at her own cleverness she ran round and round her dining room, scattering sawdust and the result of her labors in one wild whirlwind of delight.

"Olga da Polga?" exclaimed the voice of Mrs. Sawdust. "Written on the floor? Don't be silly . . . how *could* it have been?"

A face appeared at Olga's door. "I can't see anything at all. You must have been dreaming. All the same"—there was a pause—"it *is* rather a nice name. If I were you I'd keep it."

When they were alone again, Olga looked out of her window at Karen Sawdust and Karen Sawdust looked back at her.

"Grownups!" said Karen with a sigh. "They *never* understand these things. Still, we know it happened, don't we?"

Olga da Polga lifted up her head proudly. "Wheeee!" she cried, in the loudest voice she could possibly manage. "Wheeee! Wheeee! Wheeeeeeeee!"

And really, there was nothing more to be said.

Questions

1. How did Olga da Polga let Karen know her name?

2. Why did Olga da Polga call the Sawdust people by that name?

3. What is one important thing that may happen to Olga da Polga in her new home?

4. Answer these questions about words from the story.
   a. Is a *hutch* a drinking dish or a home for an animal?
   b. Are *inhabitants* of a pet shop the pets or the cages?
   c. Would a *reassuring* murmur make you feel scared or peaceful?

Activity   Write a Jobs List

Karen needs a Jobs List. The list should tell what Karen should do every day to care for Olga da Polga. Write at least four important jobs on Karen's list.

Caring for Olga da Polga

1.

2.

3.

4.

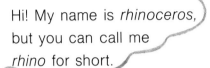

Where did you get that name?

Hi! My name is *rhinoceros,* but you can call me *rhino* for short.

CONNECTIONS

Names and Their Meanings

Animal Names

How did animals get their names? Some animals were named from words that describe them. The *rhinoceros* (ry•NOS•ur•us) got its name that way. More than two thousand years ago, Greeks marched into India. There they saw a large animal that was new to them. It had a horn on its nose. The Greeks wondered what to call this great beast. They made up the name *rhinokeras* from two Greek words. The words are *rhino,* meaning "nose," and *kersos,* meaning "horn." The name *rhinoceros* came from that first name, *rhinokeras.*

The rhino's horn is not what it appears to be. Instead of being bony, the horn is made of hairs! The hairs are packed tightly together. If the horn breaks, the rhinoceros can grow a new one.

The *moose* was named by a word that tells how it eats. Algonquian (al•GONG•kwee•un) Indians saw that this animal strips tree branches bare. They named the animal *moosu.* The word means "he strips off" or "he eats off."

Study the pictures of the animals below. Read about their names. Decide why each animal was given its name.

Armadillo is a Spanish word meaning "little armored one."

Giraffe comes from an Arabic word that means "one who walks swiftly."

Bear comes from the Old English word *bera,* meaning "brown."

Porcupine comes from two Latin words: *porcus,* "pig," and *spina,* "spine" or "thorn."

pitcher plant

ghost flower

Plant Names

Like animal names, names for plants often describe the plants. The leaves of the *pitcher plant* look like the spout of a pitcher. The leaves hold water, too. Rain falls into them and collects there. Insects come to eat the sweet liquid on the upper leaves. The insects slip down inside the "pitcher" and drown. They become the plant's food.

The *ghost flower* grows in dark forests. It is white and strange looking. Many people call this plant the *Indian pipe*. It looks like a little, long-stemmed Indian peace pipe.

Plants called *cattails* grow in marshy areas. These plants have fuzzy brown tips that really do look like cats' tails. The fuzz is made of tiny brown flowers.

cattails

214

The *sunflower* bloom looks like the sun.
The bloom turns to follow the sun from
sunrise to sunset, too. Long ago, the
Greeks told a story about how there came
to be a sunflower.

The story tells of Clytie (CLY·tee), a
water maiden. One day she left the ocean.
She climbed to the top of Mount Olympus
(oh·LIM·pus), which was the home of the
gods. There she saw the sun god, Apollo.
Clytie fell in love with him, but Apollo
loved another, which made Clytie sad.

Clytie sank to the ground. She turned
her face to the sun. She watched the sun
travel across the sky, day after day. After
many days, she grew roots. She changed
into a flower—a sunflower.

Tallahassee
FLORIDA

Chicago
ILLINOIS

NEBRASKA
Omaha

Topeka
KANSAS

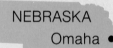
WASHINGTON
Walla Walla

Place Names

The names of places are bits of history. They often give clues about who settled in a place. In the United States, names like *New England* and *New Hampshire* tell of people who left an old home for a new one. Spanish and French names recall early explorers and settlers. City names like *Washington* and *Lincoln* honor people who are important in United States history. American Indian names remind us of the first Americans.

About half the states have American Indian names. *Kansas* means "a breeze near the ground." *Michigan* means "great water." *Texas* means "friends." *Idaho* means "good morning." The chart below gives some more American Indian place names and their meanings.

Place Name	Meaning
Tallahassee (Florida)	"old town"
Chicago (Illinois)	"wild onion place"
Omaha (Nebraska)	"those who go upstream"
Topeka (Kansas)	"good place to dig roots"
Walla Walla (Washington)	"much water"

Many places in the South and Southwest have Spanish names. Look at this map of New Mexico. Find the *Rio Grande* (REE·oh grand). This name means "great river" in Spanish. The capital, *Santa Fe,* means "holy faith." *Los Alamos* (los Al·uh·mos) means "poplar trees."

NEW MEXICO

Los Alamos

Santa Fe

Rio Grande

Here are some other Spanish place names.

Las Vegas (Nevada) means "the meadows."

Savannah (Georgia) means "treeless plain."

El Paso (Texas) was first called *El Paso del Rio.* It means "a place where the river can be crossed by wading."

French settlers also gave place names to this country. *Vermont* comes from two French words: *vert* (VAIRT), meaning "green," and *mont,* meaning "mountain." *Baton Rouge* (Louisiana) was named from two French words: *baton,* meaning "stick," and *rouge,* meaning "red." Its name means "red stick." The city was named Baton Rouge because Indians put a red stick there to mark a boundary.

Lincoln
NEBRASKA

Madison
WISCONSIN

Carson City
NEVADA

Houston
TEXAS

The names of famous people also dot the U.S. map. Many countries or cities and towns are named for presidents, such as *Washington, Lincoln, Jefferson, Monroe,* and *Madison. Dallas* (Texas) and *Fairbanks* (Alaska) were named after vice presidents. *Carson City,* Nevada, was named for the Western scout Kit Carson. *Houston* (HYOOS·tun), Texas, was named for General Sam Houston, who fought for Texas to be free from Mexico.

Some American place names seem to have no special history. The names of towns like *Polka Dot* (Ohio), *Sleepy Eye* (Minnesota), and *Frostproof* (Florida) may have been made up just for fun!

Questions

1. Why does each name fit the animal?
   a. armadillo   c. bear
   b. giraffe   d. porcupine

2. Why does each name suit the way the flower looks?
   a. Indian pipe   b. sunflower

Activities

1. **Write Animal Names**

    Make up new names for these three animals. Your names should describe something about the animals. For example, you might call these animals *Hanging Nose, Mountain Back,* and *Big Slinker.*

2. **Find Out About Your State**

    Look in an encyclopedia under the name of your state. Find out how your state got its name. Find the names of your state tree and flower. Tell why you think these plants were chosen for your state.

3. **Find Place Names on the Map**

    Look at a map of your state or your community. List names that you think are American Indian. List names that might have come from other languages or from the names of early settlers.

4. **Write a Story About a Place Name**

    Read these names of places in Mt. Rainier National Park in Washington. Choose the name of one place. Write a story about how it might have been named.

Crystal Mountain
Iron Mountain
Scarface Mountain
Silver Falls
Eagle Peak
Pyramid Peak

Oliphaunt

A poem by J. R. R. Tolkien

Gray as a mouse,
Big as a house,
Nose like a snake,
I make the earth shake,
As I tramp through the grass;
Trees crack as I pass.
With horns in my mouth
I walk in the South,
Flapping big ears.
Beyond count of years
I stump round and round,
Never lie on the ground,
Not even to die.
Oliphaunt am I,
Biggest of all,
Huge, old, and tall.
If ever you'd met me,
You wouldn't forget me.
If you never do,
You won't think I'm true;
But old Oliphaunt am I,
And I never lie.

Picture by Sharon Harker

BOOKSHELF

Whose Cat Is That? by Virginia Kahl. Charles Scribner's Sons, 1979. A small white cat wants to find a home but instead finds seven. Now she has to pretend to be seven cats with seven different names.

I Have Four Names for My Grandfather by Kathryn Lasky. Little, Brown, 1976. A grandfather is a special person to this young boy.

In a Pickle and Other Funny Idioms by Marvin Terban. Clarion Books, 1983. This book explains why we say that we "let the cat out of the bag" or that we "got it straight from the horse's mouth" and other sayings.

Benjy and the Power of Zingies by Jean Van Leeuwen. Dial Press, 1982. Third-grader Benjy is tired of being small for his age. He decides to eat the breakfast cereal of sports stars to make himself stronger.

Thumbelina by Hans Christian Anderson. Dial Press, 1979. A girl no bigger than your thumb is named Thumbelina. Though small, she has many big adventures.

4 You Can't Catch Me

The Cat Came Back

A folk song adapted by Dahlov Ipcar

There was an old yellow cat
    had troubles all her own.
No one seemed to want her,
    but she wouldn't leave her home.
They tried everything they knew
    to drive that cat away.
They took her to Alaska,
    and they told her for to stay—

BUT

The cat came back,
She couldn't stay no longer.
The cat came back,
'Cause she couldn't stay away.
The cat came back,
We thought she was a goner,
But the cat came back

ON THE VERY NEXT DAY!

Pictures by Julie Peterson

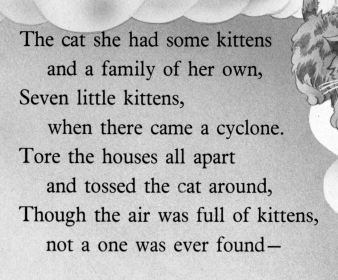

The cat she had some kittens
    and a family of her own,
Seven little kittens,
    when there came a cyclone.
Tore the houses all apart
    and tossed the cat around,
Though the air was full of kittens,
    not a one was ever found—

BUT

The cat came back,
She couldn't stay no longer.
The cat came back,
'Cause she couldn't stay away.
The cat came back,
We thought she was a goner,
But the cat came back

ON THE VERY NEXT DAY!

Then they took her to Cape Canaveral
    and found that cat a place
Right inside a rocket
    that was heading into space.
They thought that when she reached the moon,
    they'd really have it made,
But the cat returned in triumph
    for a ticker tape parade!

Oh, the cat came back!
She couldn't stay no longer.
The cat came back,
'Cause she couldn't stay away.
The cat came back,
We thought she was a goner,
But the cat came back

ON THE VERY NEXT DAY!

Animal Travelers

Something told the wild geese
   It was time to go.
Though the fields lay golden
   Something whispered, "Snow."
     . . .
Something told the wild geese
   It was time to fly—
Summer sun was on their wings,
   Winter in their cry.
          —Rachel Field

Pictures by Larry Frederick and Joanna Adamska Koperska

Summer is over in the northern part of
the world. The days are getting shorter.
The weather is cooler. It is time for many
animals to be on the move. They must
head south now to escape the harsh winter
that lies ahead.

Flocks of *Canadian geese* gather at their
nesting places. They circle in the air. Then
they fly south. Some will fly as far south
as Mexico. When snow falls in the north,
the geese will be settled in their warm,
winter homes. They will be able to find
food all winter.

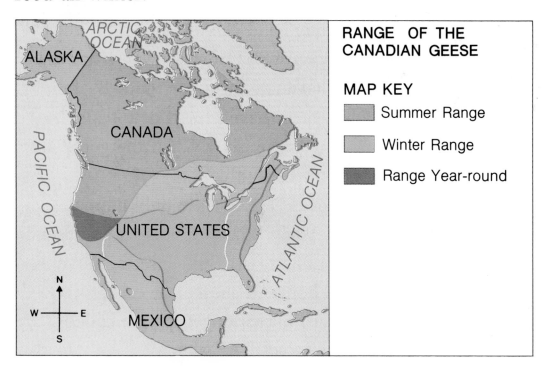

RANGE OF THE
CANADIAN GEESE

MAP KEY

Summer Range

Winter Range

Range Year-round

The geese will return in the spring. They will fly back to their nesting places, where they will lay their eggs and raise their young. The geese return north to raise their families because summer days are longer there. Parent geese need the extra hours of daylight to find food for their hungry babies.

In summer the adult geese lose their flight feathers and cannot fly. They must keep to open water to stay away from the animals that hunt them for food. By fall, the adult geese have grown new feathers. The young geese can fly. All the geese are ready to travel south.

Wild geese are not the only animal travelers. Many kinds of animals, including birds, mammals, fish, and insects, move from one home to another at certain times of the year. These long trips are called *migrations* (my·GRAY·shunz).

The longest migrations on land are made by members of the deer family. *Caribou* (KAIR·ih·boo) live in the Arctic. In the fall they gather in herds of thousands of animals. Then they move south to find food. Caribou travel up to eight hundred miles from their summer homes. In spring they return north. They follow routes caribou have taken for hundreds of years.

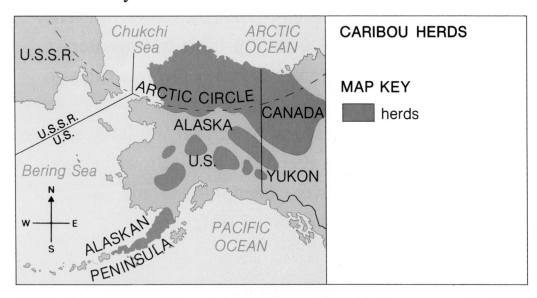

CARIBOU HERDS

MAP KEY

herds

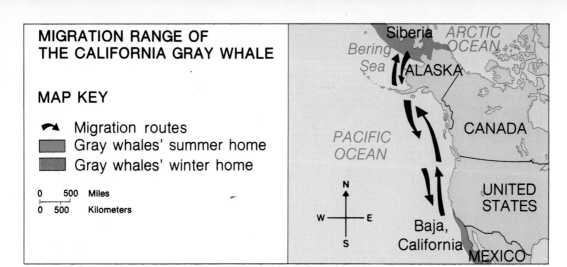

MIGRATION RANGE OF THE CALIFORNIA GRAY WHALE

MAP KEY

🐋 Migration routes
▨ Gray whales' summer home
■ Gray whales' winter home

0   500 Miles
0   500 Kilometers

Siberia ARCTIC OCEAN
Bering Sea
ALASKA
PACIFIC OCEAN
CANADA
UNITED STATES
Baja, California
MEXICO

N
W — E
S

The world's largest migrators travel through the seas. They are the *whales.* The map shows the migration path of the California gray whale. Each year gray whales make a round trip of eight thousand miles.

In summer the whales stay near Alaska, where they find plenty of food—crabs, fish, and shrimps. When fall comes they head south, to Baja (BAH·ha), California. They have their young in these warm waters. When summer comes the gray whales go north again.

Animals migrate by air, by land, and by sea. Year after year, they follow the same paths between their summer and winter homes—the animal travelers.

Questions

1. Why do Canadian geese fly south in the fall? Why do they fly north in the spring?

2. What does the word *migration* mean?

3. Why do caribou migrate?

4. Where do gray whales go to have their young?

bobolink

osprey

Activity   **Make a Migration Report**

Choose one of the animals from the list below. Find out about its travels and report on what you find. You may wish to use a map to show the class the path the animal takes. Use encyclopedias and other library books to find the information you need.

bat	bobolink	Arctic tern
seal	swallow	hummingbird
eel	polar bear	whooping crane
robin	penguin	monarch butterfly
osprey	salmon	green sea turtle

green sea turtle

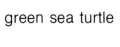

whooping crane

233

Dance of the Animals

A play adapted from a Puerto Rican folk tale retold by Pura Belpré
Pictures by Willi K. Baum

Glossary of Spanish Words

amiga mía (ah•MEE•gah MEE•ah) My friend.
amigo (ah•MEE•goh) Friend.
buenos días (BWAY•nohs THEE•ahs) Good day.
gracias (GRAH•see•ahs) Thank you.
hola (OH•lah) Hello.
jotas (HOH•tahs) Traditional Spanish dances.
señor (sen•YOHR) Sir, mister.
señora (sen•YOHR•ah) Lady, madam.
sí (SEE) Yes.

234

Characters

Narrator 1	Señor Lion	Señor Dog
Narrator 2	Señora Lioness	Señora Dog
Narrator 3	Señora Mare	Señor Goat
Narrator 4	Señora Donkey	

Setting: In the forest.

SCENE ONE

Narrator 1: Once upon a time, a lion and a lioness lived together near a great forest. Among their neighbors were Señor Horse and Señora Mare, Señor and Señora Donkey, Señor Bull and Señora Cow, Señor and Señora Dog, and Señor and Señora Goat.

Times were hard for Señor Lion and Señora Lioness, and soon the day came when they faced each other with nothing to fix for a meal.

Señora Lioness: We must do something. If times keep up like this, we shall certainly die. We cannot let that happen, for are we not the strongest beasts in the forest? Has it not been said that the bigger fish shall eat the smaller?

Señor Lion: True enough. Something must be done.

Narrator 1: Señor Lion set to thinking for a while. A short time later, an idea came to him.

Señor Lion: I have it. And a splendid idea it is, even if I have to say it myself. Listen. Which meat do we like the best?

Señora Lioness: Goat's meat.

Señor Lion: Right. It is the finest, the juiciest and certainly the tastiest. Ah, *Señora mía,* you shall see.

Señora Lioness: But how are we going to get such fresh and delicious meat?

Señor Lion: I will tell you. Listen carefully. We shall give a ball—a grand ball. And we shall invite our friends to come to it. You, who are so well liked, will ask our neighbors, and they will not refuse. We will build a roasting pit. Everyone will be dancing. And when the goats get close to the pit, I will push them into the hot coals. The rest depends on me. How do you like my plan?

Narrator 1: Señora Lioness thought for a while, at first shaking her head slowly as if the plan did not meet with her approval. Then suddenly she realized what it meant.

Señora Lioness: What a good idea! Meat at last.

Señor Lion: You will have to hurry if my plans are to be carried out.

Narrator 1: Señora Lioness went out to invite the neighbors, while Señor Lion stayed home to prepare for the big affair.

SCENE TWO

Señora Lioness: *Hola!* Señora Mare!

Señora Mare: *Hola!* Señora Lioness. What are you doing around these parts, my good friend?

Señora Lioness: I came to invite you to a dance. You and Señor Horse have such fine long legs and such strong hoofs. We need you for our orchestra. Could you not come and play the drum?

Señora Mare: Oh, most certainly. Only yesterday was I saying that we needed a little recreation. Yes, we will come and play the drum.

Señora Lioness: *Gracias.*

Narrator 2: And Señora Lioness went on her way. Pretty soon she found Señora Donkey.

Señora Lioness: Ah, *amiga mía.* I was coming to see you. We are giving a ball and would like to have you and Señor Donkey come. Señor Horse and Señora Mare are coming to play the drum. Won't you and Señor Donkey come and play the trombone?

Señora Donkey: Why, yes, Señora Lioness, we will be there without fail.

Señora Lioness: *Gracias, gracias.*

Narrator 2: On went Señora Lioness, faster and faster as she felt the pangs of hunger in her empty stomach. She had not had goat's meat in such a long time. She crossed lane after lane inviting more and more neighbors. She gave each invitation with such graciousness that those invited felt that the dance would not be a success unless they accepted.

Señora Lioness found Señor and Señora Dog sitting under the shade of a great tree. She greeted them a little breathless, for she had walked quite a distance now.

Señora Lioness: *Hola, amigos.* There is a great ball at our place tonight. You must both come.

Señor Dog: I will go, but Señora Dog stays home.

Señora Dog: I will go, too.

Señor Dog: No! No!

Señora Dog: *Sí! Sí!*

Señora Lioness: Oh, my friends, I must leave you to decide the matter yourselves. I must call on Señor Goat.

Señor Dog: Wait, Señora Lioness. Señor Goat is my best friend. I will take you to him.

Narrator 2: Once at Señor Goat's place, Señor Dog took him aside and suggested that he go alone to the dance. Señor Goat agreed.

Señor Dog: Señora Lioness, thank you for your kind invitation. Señor Goat and I will gladly come. The Señoras, however, will stay home.

Narrator 2: Señora Lioness left with a sad heart, for Señor Goat would not provide enough meat for two.

Señora Lioness (*To herself*): Oh, what will Señor Lion say when he learns that only Señor Goat is coming? Señor Goat is so small and thin.

SCENE THREE

Narrator 3: Señora Lioness soon reached home.
Señor Lion had dug a roasting pit in which hot
coals burned brightly.

Señor Lion: Well, you are here at last. Are they all
coming?

Señora Lioness: Yes, all—that is, except. . . .

Narrator 3: Señora Lioness never finished the
sentence, for so excited was Señor Lion that
he danced for joy and then went to tend the
fire. Señora Lioness had hardly finished putting
on her garland of flowers when the first guests
arrived.

Señor Lion: *Buenos días,* Señor and Señora Donkey.

Señora Donkey: What a beautiful garland! And how becoming.

Señora Lioness: *Gracias,* my friend.

Narrator 3: More guests arrived, all clean and looking their very best. Señora Cat had woven a bunch of honeysuckle on a blue ribbon around her neck. Señor Bull and Señora Cow had threaded grey and red wreaths around their horns. Last came Señor Dog and Señor Goat. Señor Lion greeted them.

Señor Lion: And where are the Señoras? Aren't they coming?

Señor Goat: No.

Señor Dog: Oh, no.

Narrator 3: Señor Lion leaned over and whispered to his wife.

Señor Lion: My dear, we shall have to eat them both, since Señora Goat did not come.

Narrator 3: Señor Lion and Señora Lioness opened
the dance. The couples whirled, stamped, and
bellowed. What tangos and *jotas!* Waltzes
mixed with mazurkas and traditional dances.

What a mixture of sounds! Señor Dog
barked and howled. Señor and Señora Cat
meowed, while the constant stamping of Señor
Donkey and the brays of Señora Mare filled the
place.

Suddenly on one of the turns of the dance
Señor Goat and Señor Dog spied the fire
in the pit.

Señor Goat: *Amigo*, I do not like the look of that fire. Let us go, for this fire is meant for us. No doubt, Señor Lion means to eat us.

Narrator 3: Then, through the dancers they pulled and pushed, skipping all the time until they reached the woods.

Señor Dog: Hurry, *amigo!* Now we must run just as fast as we possibly can.

Narrator 3: Meanwhile, at the ball things went on as before. Suddenly Señor Lion missed Señor Dog and Señor Goat. As quickly as he could without causing suspicion, he left and followed Señor Dog's and Señor Goat's trail.

SCENE FOUR

Narrator 4: The afternoon was cool and the air was heavy with the scent of the acacia trees in full bloom. The wind began to blow and with it came rain, slowly at first and then in great torrents. The river soon was swollen with the sudden downpour.

Señor Dog: *Amigo,* I am going to swim across the river. Come! Follow me.

Señor Goat (*To himself, as he stands by the bank of the river*): Señor Lion will soon be here and I cannot swim. Oh, for a good safe hiding place! Ah, perhaps I can hide in that stack of hay.

Narrator 4: No sooner had Señor Goat hidden himself and Señor Dog made his way across the river, than Señor Lion appeared. On the other side of the river, Señor Dog stood, happily jumping around and mocking Señor Lion.

Señor Lion (*Picking up and throwing a large stone*): Watch out, Señor Dog!

Señor Dog: Oh, my friend, see that bundle of straw near you? Why don't you try to throw a piece of that at me?

Señor Lion: One piece, indeed. I will throw the whole stack at you.

Narrator 4: And Señor Lion leaned forward and
tried to pick up the heavy bundle of hay. But
he only slipped and fell on his back. At this
Señor Dog leaped up and barked for joy.

Señor Dog: Try again, my friend.

Narrator 4: Señor Lion got up and tugged at the
straw bundle again. He pulled and pulled and
finally managed to lift it and hurl it across the
river. No sooner did it land on the ground than
Señor Goat jumped out of his hiding place.
And accompanied by Señor Dog, he began to
leap joyfully in the air.

Señor Goat: Señor Lion, thanks for helping me over. If I did lose most of my tail, my life, indeed, I saved.

Narrator 4: Señor Lion's rage had no limit and, looking down at his paws, he discovered that he had a large amount of fur entangled in his claws. Then he laughed.

Señor Lion: So you have, my friend, but by your stump you'll tell your tale.

Narrator 4: And it is true, because even to this day most goats have only a stump for a tail.

Questions

1. Read these riddles about the animals in the story. Which animal fits each one?
   a. I did not go to the dance. I'm glad now because I can't swim.
   b. Everyone likes me, and I like others—especially goats!
   c. I thought that the dance might be dangerous!
   d. My tail tells the tale.

2. Who did the cleverest planning in this story? Tell why you think so.

3. Which words mean *Buenos días*? Which words mean *Gracias*?
   a. Good day!   c. Let's eat!
   b. How pretty!   d. Thank you!

Activity Write a Riddle

Make up a riddle about a story *character* (KAIR·ik·tuhr)—a person or an animal in a story or a play. Write two or more clues. The clues might tell what the character did or said in the story.

About PURA BELPRÉ

For a long time, folk tales
all over the world have been
passed down by storytellers.
A storyteller of our own time
is Pura Belpré (PAW•rah
BEL•pray), who tells the folk
tales she heard as a child in
Puerto Rico.

While working in the New
York Public Library, Pura
Belpré told folk tales to
children. To make her stories
more lively, she began making and using puppets.
When people wanted to read the folk tales, Pura
Belpré wrote them down. Though many of the
stories are in books now, she still likes to tell the
tales with her handmade puppets.

More Books by Pura Belpré

The Rainbow-Colored Horse
Perez and Martina
The Tiger and the Rabbit

The Emperor and the Kite

A Chinese folk tale retold by Jane Yolen
Pictures by Ed Young

*The ancient sport of kite flying began
long ago in China. No one knows for certain
when or where in China kites were invented,
and no one knows who flew the first one.*

*Kites are found in many old Chinese folk
tales. In this folk tale, a stick-and-paper kite
is the favorite toy of a lonely Emperor's
daughter named Djeow Seow (jeeOH seeOW).*

Once in ancient China there lived a
princess who was the fourth daughter of the
emperor. She was very tiny. In fact she was
so tiny her name was Djeow Seow, which
means "the smallest one." And, because she
was so tiny, she was not thought very
much of—when she was thought of at all.

Her brothers, who were all older and bigger and stronger than she, were thought of all the time. And they were like four rising suns in the eyes of their father.

Her three sisters were all older and bigger and stronger than she. They were like three midnight moons in the eyes of their father.

But Djeow Seow was like a tiny star in the emperor's sight. The emperor often forgot he had a fourth daughter at all.

Every morning, when the wind came from the east past the rising sun, Djeow Seow flew her kite. And every evening, when the wind went to the west past the setting sun, she flew her kite. Her toy was like a flower in the sky.

A monk who passed the palace every day made up a poem about her kite.

My kite sails upward,
Mounting to the high heavens.
My soul goes on wings.

Each day Princess Djeow Seow thanked him for his poem. Then she went back to flying her kite.

But just as the wind is not always
peaceful, all was not peaceful in the
kingdom. There were evil men plotting
against the emperor. They crept up on him
one day when he was alone. Only Princess
Djeow Seow saw what happened.

The evil men took the emperor to a tower in the middle of a wide, treeless plain. The tower had only a single window. The men sealed the door with bricks and mortar. Then they rode back to the palace and said that the emperor was dead.

When his sons and daughters heard this, they ran away. But Djeow Seow built a hut of twigs and branches at the edge of the plain.

Every day at dawn and again at dark, she would walk across the plain to the tower. And there she would sail her stick-and-paper kite. To the kite string she tied a tiny basket filled with rice and poppyseed cakes, water chestnuts and green tea. The kite pulled the basket high, high in the air, up as high as the window in the tower. And, in this way, she kept her father alive.

So they lived for many days.

The evil men were cruel, and the people of the country were very sad.

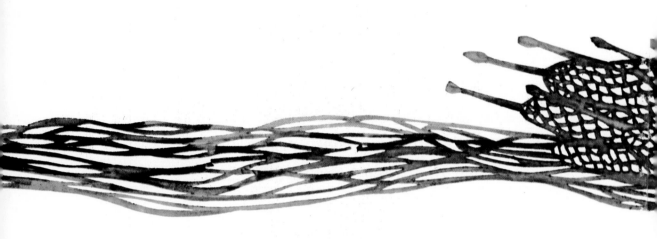

One day, as the princess prepared a basket of food for her father, the old monk passed by her hut. She smiled at him, but he seemed not to see her.

Yet, as he passed, he repeated his poem in a loud voice. He said:

> My kite sails upward,
> Mounting to the high heavens.
> My emperor goes on wings.

The princess started to thank him. But then she stopped. Something was different. The words were not quite right.

And then Djeow Seow understood. The monk was telling her something important.

Each day after that, Djeow Seow was busy. She twined a string of grass and vines, and wove in strands of her own long black hair. When her rope was as thick as her waist and as high as the tower, she was ready. She attached the rope to the string of the stick-and-paper kite, and made her way across the treeless plain.

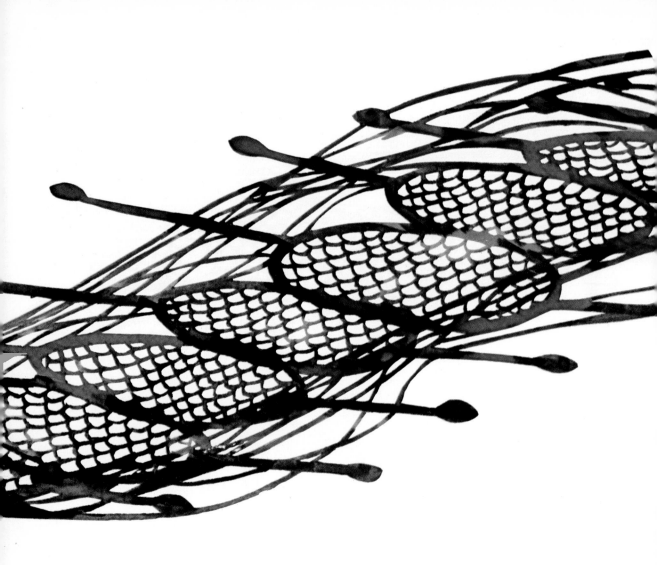

When she reached the tower, she called
to her father. But her voice was as tiny as
she, and her words were lost in the wind.

At last, though, the emperor looked out
and saw his daughter flying her kite. He
expected the tiny basket of food to sail up
to his window as it had done each day. But
what should he see but the strand of vines
and grass and long black hair. The wind
was raging above, holding the kite in its
steely grip. And the princess was below,
holding tight to the end of the rope.

The emperor leaned out of the tower
window and grasped the heavy strand. He
brought it into his tower room and
loosened the string of the kite. He set the
kite free.

Then the emperor tied one end of the thick strand to the heavy iron bar across the window, and the other end stretched all the way down to Djeow Seow's tiny hands.

The emperor stepped to the window sill and slid down the rope. His robes billowed out around him like the wings of a bright kite.

When his feet reached the ground, he knelt before his tiny daughter. And he touched the ground before her with his lips. Then he rose and embraced her, and she almost disappeared in his arms.

He lifted the tiny princess to his shoulders and carried her all the way back to the palace.

At the palace, the emperor was greeted
by wild and cheering crowds. The people
were tired of the evil men, but they had
been afraid to act. With the emperor once
again to guide them, they threw the evil
men into prison.

And when the other sons and daughters of the emperor heard of his return, they hurried home to welcome their father. When they arrived, they were surprised to find Djeow Seow on a tiny throne by their father's side.

To the end of his days, the emperor ruled with Princess Djeow Seow close by.

And, too, it is said that Djeow Seow
ruled after him, as gentle as the wind and,
in her loyalty, as unyielding.

Questions

1. Who were like four rising suns?

2. Who was like the gentle, unyielding wind?

3. What was like a flower in the sky?

4. Which word did the author use instead of each underlined word?

   evil   twined   ancient

   a. Djeow Seow lived in <u>long-ago</u> China.
   b. <u>Bad</u> men put the emperor in a tower.
   c. Djeow Seow <u>made</u> a string of grass and vines.

5. Why would this be a good story to tell to children?

Activity   Design and Write About a Kite

Djeow Seow needs a kite to fly when she is ruling the country. Design a beautiful kite for her. Then complete the sentences to tell about the kite. Compare it to something beautiful.

The kite will look like a _____.
The kite will fly like a _____.

About ED YOUNG

Do you ever daydream? When Ed Young was a boy in China, he daydreamed so much that his mother wondered what would become of him. The rest of the family, however, enjoyed the plays and the drawings Ed Young made up from his dreams.

Ed Young came to the United States to go to art school. *The Mean Mouse and Other Mean Stories* was the first book he illustrated. Since then, he has become well known as an illustrator who uses modern forms of ancient arts. In *The Emperor and the Kite,* he used the Chinese art of paper cutting.

More Books Illustrated by Ed Young

Bicycle Rider

The Girl Who Loved the Wind

The Red Lion: A Persian Story

The Rooster's Horns: A Chinese Puppet Play to
    Make and Perform

The Lion and the Mouse

Learn About

Great Escapes

Peter and the Wolf *by Sergei Prokofiev*

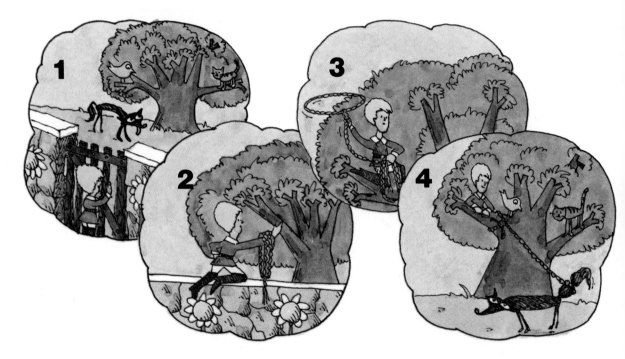

In some stories the characters get into trouble. They need a way to get out of that trouble. They need a "great escape" plan. Sometimes the characters think of their own "great escape" plans. Sometimes someone else helps them escape. In the story above, who helps the cat and the bird escape from the wolf?

270

The characters in the stories below all had "great escape" plans. Choose one or both of these stories. Tell what the plans were by answering the questions.

1. **Dance of the Animals**

   Who was in trouble?
   How did they escape?
   Who helped them escape?

2. **The Emperor and the Kite**

   Who was in trouble?
   How did he escape?
   Who helped him escape?

Now you be the author. The character
in this picture is in trouble. Draw or tell a story
about her "great escape" plan. Write a title for
your story. Begin by telling *who* the character
is and *how* her trouble began. Then tell *how*
she escaped.

The Grasshopper

A poem by David McCord

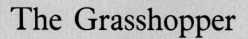

Down

a

deep

well

a

grasshopper

fell.

By kicking about

He thought to get out.

He might have known better,

For that got him wetter.

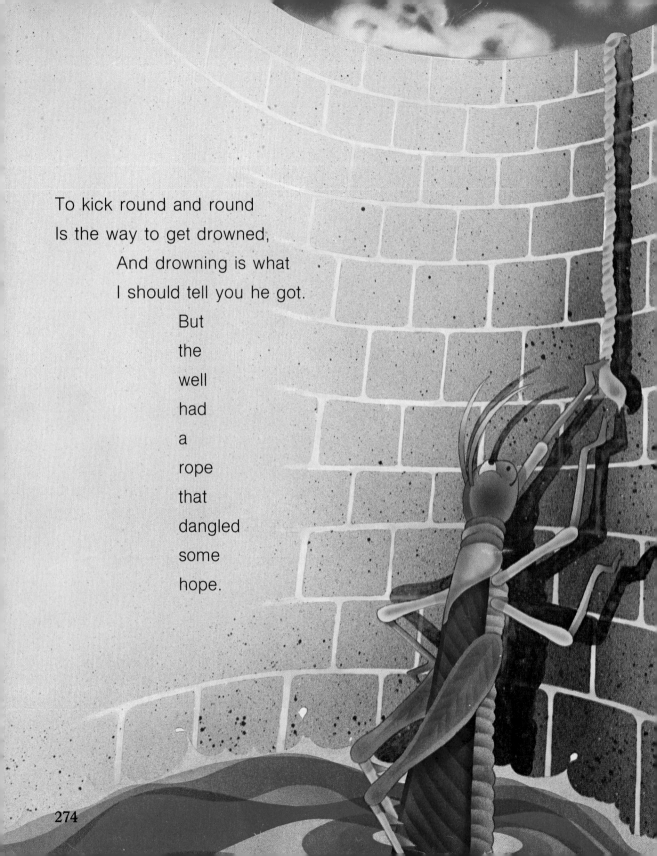

To kick round and round
Is the way to get drowned,
    And drowning is what
      I should tell you he got.
        But
        the
        well
        had
        a
        rope
        that
        dangled
        some
        hope.

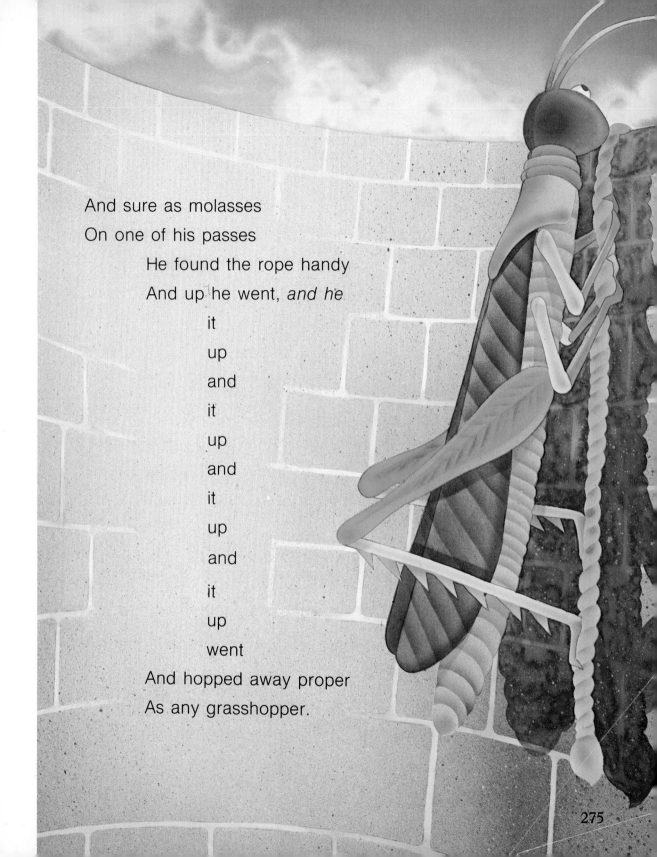

And sure as molasses
On one of his passes
    He found the rope handy
    And up he went, *and he*
        it
        up
        and
        it
        up
        and
        it
        up
        and
        it
        up
        went
And hopped away proper
As any grasshopper.

Not Me

A poem by Shel Silverstein

The Slithergadee has crawled out of the sea.
He may catch all the others, but he
   won't catch me.
No, you won't catch me, Old Slithergadee,
You may catch all the others, but you wo—

Picture by Robert Evans

My Father
and the Dragon

From the story *My Father's Dragon* by Ruth Stiles Gannett

Pictures by Don Weller

My father had an exciting adventure
when he was a boy—all because he found
an alley cat who told him about a baby
dragon. The cat had been on Wild Island
when the dragon fell from a low cloud and
injured a wing. The animals of Wild Island
captured the small dragon easily. Then the
lazy animals began forcing the dragon to fly
them across the river that divided their
island since the crocodiles in the river could
not be trusted.

My father set out to rescue the dragon.
First he sneaked aboard a ship bound for
the Island of Tangerina. From there he went
to Wild Island, where he had to outwit many
animals who wanted to eat him. At last he
got to the river. He knew the baby dragon
was on the other side.

My father walked back and forth along
the bank trying to think of some way to
cross the river. He found a high flagpole
with a rope going over to the other side. The
rope went through a loop at the top of the
pole and then down the pole and around a
large crank. A sign on the crank said:

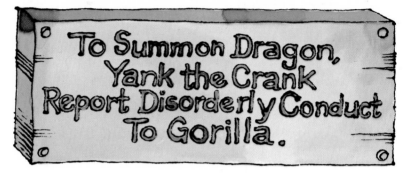

To Summon Dragon,
Yank the Crank
Report Disorderly Conduct
To Gorilla.

From what the cat had told my father, he
knew that the other end of the rope was tied
around the dragon's neck. And he felt
sorrier than ever for the poor dragon. If the
dragon was on this side, the gorilla would
twist his wings. It would hurt so much that
he'd have to fly to the other side. If he was
on the other side, the gorilla would crank
the rope until the dragon would either choke
to death or fly back to this side. What a life
for a baby dragon!

My father knew that if he called to the
dragon to come across the river, the gorilla
would surely hear him. So he thought about
climbing the pole and going across on the
rope. The pole was very high. Even if he
could get to the top without being seen, he'd
have to go all the way across hand over
hand. The river was very muddy. All sorts of
unfriendly things might live in it. But my father
could think of no other way to get across.
He was about to start up the pole when,
despite all the noise the monkeys were
making, he heard a loud splash behind him.
He looked all around in the water. But it was
dusk now, and he couldn't see anything there.

281

"It's me. Crocodile," said a voice to the left. "The water's lovely. And I have such a craving for something sweet. Won't you come in for a swim?"

A pale moon came out from behind the clouds. My father could now see where the voice was coming from. The crocodile's head was just peeping out of the water.

"Oh, no thank you," said my father. "I never swim after sundown. But I do have something sweet to offer you. Perhaps you'd like a lollipop. And perhaps you have friends who would like lollipops, too?"

"Lollipops!" said the crocodile. "Why, that is a treat! How about it, boys?"

A whole chorus of voices shouted, "Hurrah! Lollipops!" My father counted as many as seventeen crocodiles with their heads just peeping out of the water.

"That's fine," said my father. And he got out the two dozen pink lollipops and the rubber bands. "I'll stick one here in the bank. Lollipops last longer if you keep them out of the water, you know. Now, one of you can have this one."

The crocodile who had first spoken swam up and tasted it. "Delicious, mighty delicious!" he said.

"Now if you don't mind," said my father, "I'll just walk along your back and fasten another lollipop to the tip of your tail with a rubber band. You don't mind, do you?"

"Oh, no, not in the least," said the crocodile.

"Can you get your tail out of the water just a bit?" asked my father.

"Yes, of course," said the crocodile, and he lifted up his tail. Then my father ran along his back and fastened another lollipop with a rubber band.

"Who's next?" said my father. A second crocodile swam up and began sucking on that lollipop.

"Now, you gentlemen can save a lot of time if you just line up across the river," said my father. "I'll be along to give you each a lollipop."

So the crocodiles lined up right across the river. With their tails in the air, they waited for my father to fasten on the rest of the lollipops. The tail of the seventeenth crocodile just reached the other bank.

My father was crossing the back of the fifteenth crocodile with two more lollipops to go, when the noise of the monkeys suddenly stopped. He could hear a much bigger noise getting louder every second. Then he could hear seven furious tigers and one raging rhinoceros and two seething lions and one ranting gorilla along with countless screeching monkeys. They were led by two extremely angry wild boars. All were yelling, "It's a trick! It's a trick! There's an invasion and it must be after our dragon. Kill it! Kill it!" The whole crowd stampeded down to the bank.

As my father was fixing the seventeenth lollipop for the last crocodile, he heard a wild boar scream, "Look, it came this way! It's over there now, see! The crocodiles made a bridge for it." And just as my father leapt onto the other bank, one of the wild boars jumped onto the back of the first crocodile. My father didn't have a moment to spare.

By now the dragon realized that my
father was coming to rescue him. He ran out
of the bushes and jumped up and down
yelling, "Here I am! I'm right here! Can you
see me? Hurry, the boar is coming over on
the crocodiles, too. They're all coming over!
Oh, please hurry, hurry!" The noise was
simply terrible.

My father ran up to the dragon and took
out his very sharp jackknife. "Steady, old
boy, steady. We'll make it. Just stand still,"
he told the dragon as he began to saw
through the big rope.

By this time both boars, all seven tigers, the two lions, the rhinoceros, and the gorilla, along with the countless screeching monkeys, were all on their way across the crocodiles. And there was still a lot of rope to cut through.

"Oh, hurry," the dragon kept saying. My father again told him to stand still.

"If I don't think I can make it," said my father, "we'll fly over to the other side of the river. I can finish cutting the rope there."

Suddenly the screaming grew louder and madder. My father thought the animals must have crossed the river. He looked around, and saw something which surprised and delighted him. Partly because he had finished his lollipop, and partly because, as I told you before, crocodiles are very moody and not the least bit dependable and are always looking for something to eat, the first crocodile had turned away from the bank. He had started swimming down the river. The second crocodile hadn't finished yet. So he followed right after the first, still sucking his lollipop. All the rest did the same thing, one right after the other, until they were all swimming away in a line. The two wild boars, the seven tigers, the rhinoceros, the two lions, the gorilla, along with the countless screeching monkeys, were all riding down the middle of the river on the train of crocodiles sucking pink lollipops, and all were yelling and screaming and getting their feet wet.

My father and the dragon laughed
themselves weak because it was such a silly
sight. As soon as they had recovered, my
father finished cutting the rope. The dragon
raced around in circles and tried to turn a
somersault. He was the most excited baby
dragon that ever lived. My father was in a
hurry to fly away. When the dragon finally
calmed down a bit, my father climbed up
onto his back.

"All aboard!" said the dragon. "Where shall we go?"

"We'll spend the night on the beach. Tomorrow we'll start on the long journey home. So, it's off to the shores of Tangerina!" shouted my father. The dragon soared above the dark jungle and the muddy river and all the animals bellowing at them and all the crocodiles licking pink lollipops and grinning wide grins.

Questions

1. How do you summon a dragon in this story?

2. How do you cross a river in this story?

3. What would be a good reason for a father to tell this story to his child?

4. Which word did the author use instead of each underlined word?

   craving   **raging**   **chorus**

   a. a <u>group</u> of voices
   b. a <u>desire</u> for sweets
   c. a <u>furious</u> rhinoceros

Activity   Write a Funny Ending

Help Glinda finish her story. Add describing words and nonsense words. Make the story funny!

"You can't catch me!" I yelled. Then I started to run. Behind me were—
    Four _____ plum-zoomers,
    Three laughing _____,
    Two _____ duffle-wompers,
    And one _____ _____.
    And they all caught me.

BOOKSHELF

Wiley and the Hairy Man by Molly Garrett Bang. Macmillan, 1976. When Wiley goes out on the Tombigbee River, he meets the Hairy Man. Wiley must find a way to escape.

The Angry Moon by William Sleator. Little, Brown, 1970. Lupan climbs into the sky on an arrow ladder to try to rescue his friend from the angry moon.

Mr. Yowder and the Steamboat by Glen Rounds. Holiday House, 1977. Mr. Yowder finds problems when he visits New York City to go fishing.

Petronella by Jay Williams. Parents' Magazine Press, 1973. Like her two brothers, Petronella sets out on an adventure. She, however, is looking for a prince to rescue.

The Three Wishes: A Collection of Puerto Rican Folktales retold by Ricardo E. Alegría. Harcourt Brace Jovanovich, 1969. Princesses and clever animals escape from danger in these fine tales.

5 Would You Believe It!

Talk

A West African folk tale retold by Harold Courlander and George Herzog
Pictures by Sarn Suvityasiri

Once, not far from the city of Accra on the
Gulf of Guinea, a country man went out to his
garden to dig up some yams to take to market.
While he was digging, one of the yams said to
him:

"Well, at last you're here. You never
weeded me, but now you come around with
your digging stick. Go away and leave me
alone!"

The farmer turned around and looked at his
cow in amazement. The cow was chewing her
cud and looking at him.

"Did you say something?" he asked.

The cow kept on chewing and said nothing, but the man's dog spoke up.

"It wasn't the cow who spoke to you," the dog said. "It was the yam. The yam says to leave him alone."

The man became angry, because his dog had never talked before, and he didn't like his tone besides. So he took his knife and cut a branch from a palm tree to whip his dog. Just then the palm tree said:

"Put that branch down!"

The man was getting very upset about the way things were going, and he started to throw the palm branch away, but the palm branch said:

"Man, put me down softly!"

He put the branch down gently on a stone, and the stone said:

"Hey, take that thing off me!"

This was enough, and the frightened farmer started to run for his village. On the way he met a fisherman going the other way with a fish trap on his head.

"What's the hurry?" the fisherman asked.

"My yam said, 'Leave me alone!' Then the
dog said, 'Listen to what the yam says!' When
I went to whip the dog with a palm branch the
tree said, 'Put that branch down!' Then the
palm branch said, 'Do it softly!' Then the stone
said, 'Take that thing off me!'"

"Is that all?" the man with the fish trap
asked. "Is that so frightening?"

"Well," the man's fish trap said, "did he
take it off the stone?"

"Wah!" the fisherman shouted. He threw
the fish trap on the ground and began to run
with the farmer, and on the trail they met a
weaver with a bundle of cloth on his head.

"Where are you going in such a rush?" he asked them.

"My yam said, 'Leave me alone!'" the farmer said. "The dog said, 'Listen to what the yam says!' The tree said, 'Put that branch down!' The branch said, 'Do it softly!' And the stone said, 'Take that thing off me!'"

"And then," the fisherman continued, "the fish trap said, 'Did he take it off?'"

"That's nothing to get excited about," the weaver said, "no reason at all."

"Oh yes it is," his bundle of cloth said. "If it happened to you you'd run too!"

"Wah!" the weaver shouted. He threw his bundle on the trail and started running with the other men.

They came panting to the ford in the river
and found a man bathing.

"Are you chasing a gazelle?" he asked them.

The first man said breathlessly:

"My yam talked at me, and it said, 'Leave
me alone!' And my dog said, 'Listen to your
yam!' And when I cut myself a branch the tree
said, 'Put that branch down!' And the branch
said, 'Do it softly!' And the stone said, 'Take
that thing off me!'"

The fisherman panted:

"And my trap said, 'Did he?'"

The weaver wheezed:

"And my bundle of cloth said, 'You'd run too!'"

"Is that why you're running?" the man in the river asked.

"Well, wouldn't you run if you were in their position?" the river said.

The man jumped out of the water and began to run with the others. They ran down the main street of the village to the house of the chief. The chief's servants brought his stool out, and he came and sat on it to listen to their complaints. The men began to recite their troubles.

"I went out to my garden to dig yams," the farmer said, waving his arms. "Then everything began to talk! My yam said, 'Leave me alone!' My dog said, 'Pay attention to your yam!' The tree said, 'Put that branch down!' The branch said, 'Do it softly!' And the stone said, 'Take it off me!'"

"And my fish trap said, 'Well, did he take it off?'" the fisherman said.

"And my cloth said, 'You'd run too!'" the weaver said.

"And the river said the same," the bather said hoarsely, his eyes bulging.

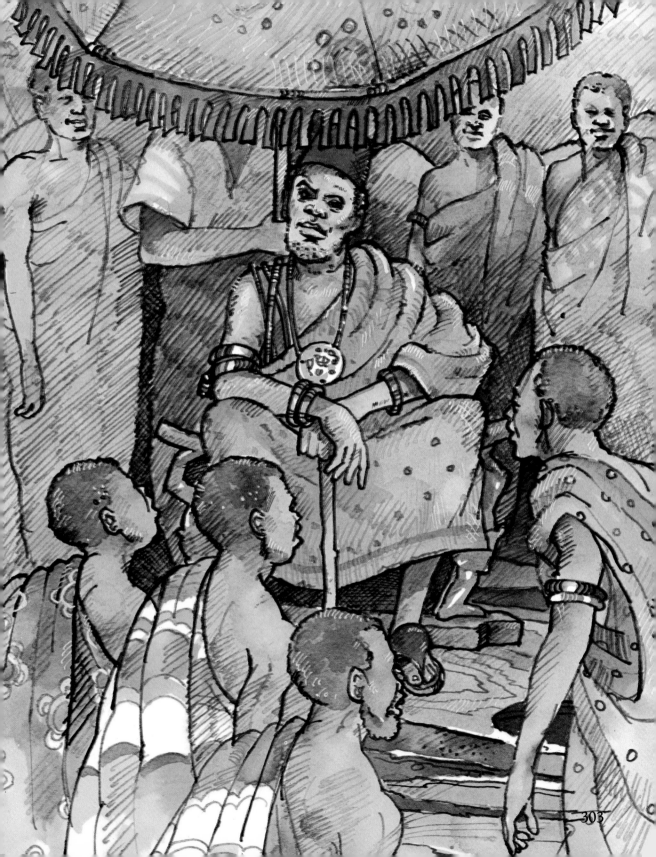

The chief listened to them patiently, but he couldn't refrain from scowling.

"Now this is really a wild story," he said at last. "You'd better all go back to your work before I punish you for disturbing the peace."

So the men went away, and the chief shook his head and mumbled to himself, "Nonsense like that upsets the community."

"Fantastic, isn't it?" his stool said. "Imagine, a talking yam!"

Questions

1. You know this story is funny because
   a. yams need weeding.   b. yams don't talk.
   c. yams taste good.

2. What might have happened after the chief's stool spoke? Tell what the chief said and did.

3. Find the words used in the story instead of the underlined words.
   a. The man put the branch down <u>gently</u>.
   b. The chief came to hear the men's <u>problems</u>.
   c. The men began to <u>tell</u> their troubles.

4. Why might someone tell the story "Talk"? Give two reasons.

Activity   Finish the Story Plan

Suppose you are getting ready to tell the story "Talk." Here is a plan to help you remember the first part of the story.

The yam talks. → The dog talks. → The tree talks. → ?

Complete this plan for the rest of the story. Remember to list the things in the order in which they happened.

Sparrow Socks

A story by George Selden
Pictures by Dan Siculan

Years ago, in a town in Scotland, there lived a little boy whose name was Angus McFee. He lived with his father, Fergus McFee, and his mother, Fiona McFee, and his two uncles, Murdoch and Hamish McFee, in a rambly house at the end of a winding old street.

There was a big garden behind the house. And high in the branches of all the trees many sparrows had their nests. When it was summer, they chirped in the sunlight and fluffed their feathers in the breeze.

But when autumn came, and the chill wind blew, they huddled down in their nests and their bills chattered.

The name of one of these sparrows was Bruce, and Bruce Sparrow was a good friend of Angus McFee.

Angus always made sure that Bruce had plenty of seeds to eat. And in warm weather he kept the birdbath full of water. Bruce and all the other sparrows liked to take a bath every day.

Angus and Bruce played tricks together sometimes too. Bruce could fly upside down and he could hide in Angus's pocket and he could stand on his head in Angus's hand. All curled up inside his feathers, he felt to Angus like a wee puff ball with a heartbeat inside it.

But there wasn't very much time for playing tricks. Every afternoon Angus had to go and help his father and his uncles in their work.

Fergus and Murdoch and Hamish McFee owned a factory that made socks. They had built a wonderful sock machine that clicked and that clacked, and that purred and that whirred. It could make long socks and short socks, and big socks and little socks, and white socks and colored socks, and summer socks and winter socks, and socks with circles on them and socks with squares on them. The wonderful sock machine could make every kind of sock in the whole world!

It was Angus's job to oil all the wheels on the wonderful sock machine and to sweep up the bits of yarn and thread that were left over at the end of each day. Angus loved his job.

But lately he had grown very worried. For the wonderful sock machine worked less and less.

The McFee brothers had only a little factory, with their own little store in front.

It was way off in a corner of the town where the streets were narrow and winding and old. Most people bought their socks from the big stores down in the center of town. And the big stores got their socks from factories all over Scotland.

Every morning Fergus McFee would meet with his two brothers. They sat at a long table in the sock factory, and they thought about socks. And they talked about socks. And they worried about socks! And they almost went out of their *minds* about socks! But they couldn't think how to sell their socks.

"What we mun have is a beauteous new sock to sell," said Fergus McFee. "A warm and woolly winter sock!"

"Ay!" said Hamish and Murdoch McFee together.

They set the wheels on the wonderful sock machine and put yarn into it. And it clicked and it clacked, and it purred and it whirred. And in a minute out came a beauteous new, warm and woolly winter sock with stripes and a bright red toe on it.

"Weel, 'tis verra pretty!" said Fergus McFee. "Now we mun hope that when cold days come, everybody will buy our socks."

"Ay, let's hope so!" said Hamish and Murdoch McFee together.

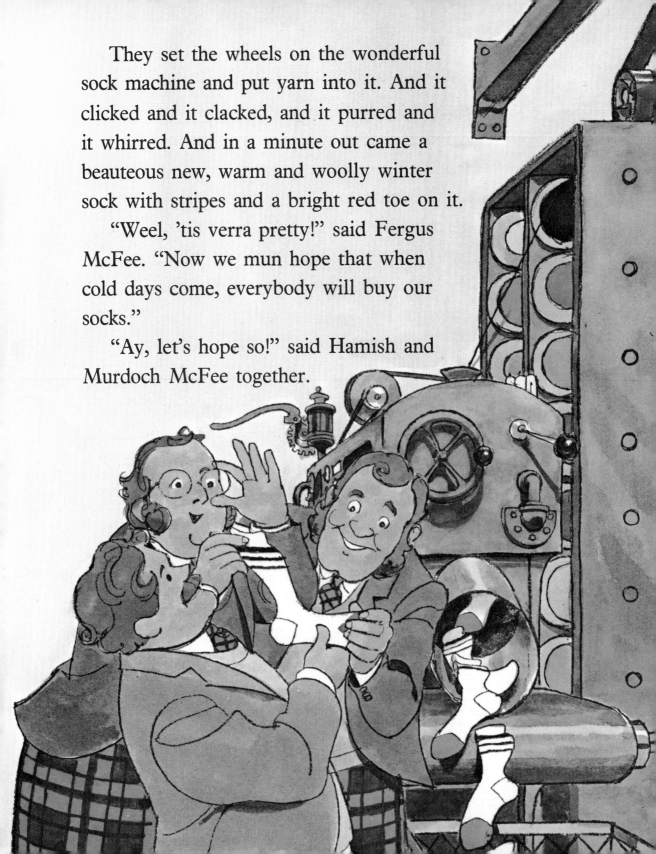

The cold days came and the chill wind blew, but everybody went to the big stores to buy their winter socks. And the wonderful sock machine worked less and less.

One morning Angus went out into the garden. Bruce Sparrow was standing on the rim of the birdbath, shivering. Overnight the water had turned to ice. He lifted first one foot and then the other.

"Are your feet cold?" said Angus. Bruce gave a chilly little chirp, and his bill chattered.

"Do you know what I think?" said Angus. "I think you need a pair of socks!" Bruce Sparrow chirped again—happily this time.

That afternoon in the sock factory, when his father and his uncles had gone home, Angus opened the pocket of his jacket. Who should be hiding there but Bruce Sparrow! "It willna take much yarn to make you a wee pair of socks," said Angus.

He set the wheels on the wonderful sock
machine so it would make the smallest pair
of socks it could. It clicked and it clacked,
and it purred and it whirred—and in a
minute out popped the tiniest wee pair of
socks in the whole world! It was the
beauteous new, warm and woolly winter
sock with the stripes and the bright red toe
on it, but small enough for a little bird to
wear.

Angus slipped the socks on Bruce
Sparrow's feet. And they fitted perfectly!

Bruce was so happy with his new socks
that he jumped up into the air and flew
upside down all around the room.

The next morning Bruce Sparrow flew from tree to tree in the garden.

"See my new socks!" he chirped to all the other sparrows. They stood on the cold branches, shivering—first on one foot, then on the other—and their bills chattered.

"We mun have socks too!" they all chirped.

That afternoon Angus was sweeping up in the sock factory. There were only a few bits of yarn and thread left over today, for the wonderful sock machine hardly worked at all. Suddenly a tap-tap-tapping sounded at the window. Angus opened it, and in flew Bruce Sparrow—with his socks on! Behind him came another sparrow, whose bill was chattering.

Bruce Sparrow chirped to introduce his friend.

And the other sparrow gave a chilly little chirp which meant "Please!"

"Oh, I see!" said Angus. "You want a wee pair of socks too."

He set the wheels on the wonderful sock machine, and in a minute the second sparrow had his own pair of socks too.

But then Angus happened to notice that up on the windowsill there was *another* little sparrow whose bill was chattering! He blinked at Angus and gave a chilly little chirp.

And when that sparrow had his own wee pair of socks, *another* one flew in! And then another! And another! And another!

Angus kept saying, "Oh, all right!" and "I guess it's all right!" and "Just one more now!" But before he knew it, he had made socks for *all* the sparrows! He couldn't say no to any bird whose bill was chattering and who gave a chilly little chirp which meant "Please!"

When they all had their new socks, the sparrows gave a big happy chirp which meant "Thank you, Angus!" Then they flew away home to their nests for the night.

Angus finished sweeping up the sock factory. He carefully oiled all the wheels on the wonderful sock machine. And he hoped that somehow it could go on working. And he went home too.

The next day was the strangest day that ever dawned in the town where Angus lived. People looked out of their windows and they saw sparrows everywhere—all wearing little pairs of beauteous new, warm and woolly winter socks with stripes and bright red toes on them!

One lady saw a sparrow pecking for seeds—with his socks on!

A man saw a sparrow pulling up a worm—with his socks on!

A little girl saw a sparrow just going for a walk on the limb of an old oak tree—with his socks on!

Everyone wanted to know where the sparrows got their socks. In a crowd they ran from one big store to another. But the owners of the big stores all said, "No, we dinna sell socks to sparrows here!"

The same morning Fergus and Hamish and Murdoch McFee went to the sock factory as usual. But they found that all their yarn had disappeared! The whole day long they hunted under tables and in closets and all around the sock factory for the yarn. They were so busy hunting that they didn't see any of the sparrows.

In the afternoon Angus arrived with Bruce Sparrow riding in his pocket. He found his father and his uncles sitting at the long table with gloomy faces.

"Someone has stolen our yarn," his father said. "It's all gone!"

"Oh, dear," said Angus. "It mun be the socks I made for the sparrows!"

"You made socks for *whom?*" said his father and his uncles all at once.

Angus told them what he had done. "They were all so verra cold," he explained.

His father only shook his head. "Weel, the yarn's gone now," he sighed.

Bruce Sparrow heard all that was said. He crept out of Angus's pocket, and when no one was looking, he flew out the window.

From tree to tree he went, until he had gathered all the sparrows together.

"We mun give back our socks," he chirped. "Angus used up all the yarn."

"But we dinna *want* to give back our socks!" the sparrows chirped. "We *like* our socks!"

"Ay," said Bruce, "but we got Angus in trouble. So we mun give them back. Everybody follow me."

In a long line all the sparrows flew to the sock factory, in through the window and down onto the table. Then they all began to take their socks off. It was hard work, with only wings to work with, but they pulled with their bills and finally got all their socks off.

Angus and his father and his uncles were amazed! They just stood back and watched.

When their socks were off, the sparrows piled them up in a neat pile on the table. They all gave a big chirp together, which meant "Thanks anyway!"

Just then there came a loud knock-knock-knocking at the door. Angus opened it, and a crowd of people rushed in.

"There are the sparrows and there are their socks!" they all shouted, and they gazed in wonder.

It was the first time this many people had ever been in the sock factory. As long as they all were there, Angus just thought he would ask them something.

"Wouldna all you people like some beauteous new, warm and woolly winter socks with stripes and bright red toes on them?" he said. "We could make them just like the sparrows' socks but big enough for people."

At first no one said anything. Then a wee voice at the back of the crowd said, "Mother, I mun have a pair of Sparrow Socks!"

And another wee voice said, "Mother, so mun I!"

And then everyone began to shout at once.

"Socks!"

"Socks!"

"SOCKS!"

"We all mun have our Sparrow Socks!"

Well, the McFee brothers had never had so many customers in their lives. "Angus," said his father, "give all the sparrows back their socks! They deserve them!" Then Fergus sent Hamish and Murdoch running off to buy more yarn.

Angus slipped their socks back on the sparrows' feet. And while everyone was waiting for the yarn, the sparrows marched around the long table in a sparrow parade— with their socks on!

And now the wonderful sock machine goes click and goes clack, and it purrs and it whirrs all day long!

For all the people in that town—and the dogs and cats too—are wearing their own pairs of beauteous new, warm and woolly Sparrow Socks with stripes and bright red toes on them!

Questions

1. What was Angus's job?

2. When do you first know that "Sparrow Socks" is a make-believe story, not a true one? Copy the first sentence that tells you.

3. Suppose Angus said, "We advertised." Which event below shows what he means? What happened as a result?
   a. The machine made beauteous socks.
   b. People saw the sparrows wearing the socks Angus made.
   c. The sparrows piled their socks on the table.

4. In Scotland someone says, "I dinna sing verra weel." What does that mean?

Activity   Make a Diagram

I am a wonderful sock machine. I can click, clack, purr, and whirr. Draw me. Label my parts. Make your drawing and your labels show how I work.

Adventures of Isabel

From the poem by Ogden Nash

Isabel met an enormous bear,
Isabel, Isabel, didn't care.
The bear was hungry, the bear was ravenous,
The bear's big mouth was cruel and cavernous.
The bear said, Isabel, glad to meet you,
How do, Isabel, now I'll eat you!
Isabel, Isabel, didn't worry;
Isabel didn't scream or scurry.
She washed her hands and she straightened her
   hair up,
Then Isabel quietly ate the bear up.

Picture by Susan Jaekel

323

The Big Wind of '34

A tall tale by James Flora
Pictures by Marie-Louise Gay

If you stay around Grandpa long enough, you will hear all sorts of amazing stories about his farm. Some people might call them tall tales, but you can decide for yourself after reading this tale as Grandpa tells it.

When Grandma and I first came to the farm, there was no barn—just a house. We were very poor and couldn't afford to build a barn. We had a cow, and she had to sleep outside. She didn't like that at all. On cold days she would get so angry that she wouldn't give us any milk.

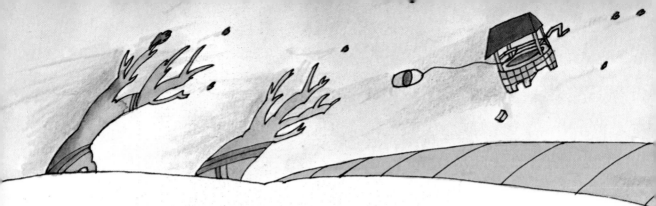

We tried to explain to the cow how sorry we were, but she wouldn't listen. When a cow gets good and mad, she just won't listen to anybody.

Then one day in 1934 the wind started to blow. Oh, my! How it did blow! Harder and harder until it blew all the leaves off the trees. Stronger and stronger until it blew the trees away, too. I had to tie down the cow or she would have been carried away. Even so, she sailed around in the sky like a big cow kite.

I've never seen such a strong wind in my whole life. I had just finished digging a deep well in the backyard. I had to dig it down forty feet, and that was hard work. But that wind huffed and puffed until it blew the well right out of the ground and carried it away. I never did see it again.

That made me so mad that I ran out of the house and threw a big chunk of firewood at the wind. It must have hurt him. It must have made him stop and think how mean he was being to Grandma and me, because the next thing I saw was a big blue barn sailing through the air. It swished over the house and settled there where you see it now. It was a good barn, but it didn't have any doors. So I shouted:

"HEY, WIND! YOU FORGOT THE DOORS!"

That old wind turned right around and
blew back to wherever he had come from.
In no time at all, I could hear him coming
back. Sure enough, he had the doors for
the barn. And he even fetched the pigeon
house you see on top.

When the wind had gone, I went out
and looked around that fine barn. It was
just what I wanted. The only trouble was
that it had settled on our cow's tail and
broken it off. That made me very sad, but
Grandma said not to worry. She said she
had cow salve that would fix everything.
But that's another story, which I will tell
you some day.

Questions

1. What are two things the Big Wind of '34 did?

2. Grandma says, "Grandpa told a *tall tale* about the wind." What does she mean?
   a. His story was wild and unbelievable.
   b. His story really did happen.
   c. His story was very long.

3. Which cow would you find in a *tall tale*?
   a. a cow that hid behind a bush
   b. a cow that gave orange juice
   c. a cow that frightened away a robber

4. Grandma said she would put *salve* on the cow's tail. Is salve a string, a kind of medicine, or a kind of cloth?

Activity   Write a Tall Tale Title

Write an exciting *tall tale title* for this year: "The _____ of _____." Draw or paint a picture to go with your title. Then write the beginning sentences of your tall tale.

Wind Power

On a windy day, the wind pushes against you. You hear it groan and howl. The wind is like an invisible giant. You cannot see the wind, but it has great and surprising power.

The Wild Wind

Wind power sometimes does strange things. Here are some of them.

- A strong north wind blew down the Rhone Valley in France. It picked up rocks and hurled them through windows.
- The north wind once pushed a string of railroad cars twenty-five miles before the cars could be stopped.

Pictures by Jack Wallen

- During a tornado, wind drove a wheat straw into an oak tree.
- In 1928 hurricane winds hit Lake Okeechobee (OH·kee·CHOH·bee) in Florida. The winds blew the lake's waters onto its shore. That was about eight billion tons of water!
- Windstorms have scooped up ponds, then dropped them somewhere else. People are surprised to see it "rain" fish and frogs.

- In 1937 a tornado picked up a train locomotive. It plunked the locomotive down, facing the other way, on another railroad track.
- In Kansas a tornado picked up a long barbed-wire fence. Then it rolled the fence up neatly before dropping it.

Using Wind Power

Wind power can be harmful, but it can be helpful, too. Thousands of years ago someone hung the first sail on a boat. People have been using wind power ever since. For centuries, wind was the main way of moving boats across the seas and oceans of the world.

Today most ships are powered by engines that burn fuel. Fuel is expensive, however, so some ship builders have tried going back to wind power.

Jacques-Yves Cousteau (zhahk•EEV koo•STOH) is an ocean explorer. He has a boat that is powered by the wind. A tall tube, with a flap along its side, is the boat's "sail." A computer turns the flap to catch the wind.

On land, wind power pushes the blades of machines called *windmills*. A hundred years ago there were many windmills in the United States. Windmills ground grain into flour. They pumped drinking water. Then electric power took over these jobs. Windmills were no longer used.

Now people are starting to build windmills again. Scientists are working on new and better windmills. Someday giant windmills may make electricity for homes and factories. As long as the wild wind blows, people will try to capture its power and make it serve their needs.

Questions

1. Most sailboats do not depend on wind power alone. They have fuel-powered engines, too. Why do sailboats need engines as well as sails?

2. What is one way in which wind power can be harmful?

3. What is one way in which wind power can be helpful?

Activities

1. **Invent New Uses for Windmills**

   Invent a new use for the windmill. What will you have the windmill do? Will you have the windmill run a car? wash the dishes? brush your teeth? Draw a picture of your invention. Then write about how your invention works.

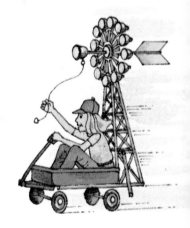

2. **Write Wind Poems**

   What sounds does the wind make? What words tell about the wind? Use words you know or make up new words that tell about the wind and its sounds. Make a list of these words. Then use them in a poem.

Eat-It-All Elaine

A poem by Kaye Starbird

I went away last August
To summer camp in Maine,
And there I met a camper
Called Eat-it-all Elaine.
Although Elaine was quiet,
She liked to cause a stir
By acting out the nickname
Her camp-mates gave to her.

The day of our arrival
At Cabin Number Three
When girls kept coming over
To greet Elaine and me,
She took a piece of paper
And calmly chewed it up,
Then strolled outside the cabin
And ate a buttercup.

Elaine, from that day forward,
Was always in command.
On hikes, she'd eat some birch-bark.
On swims, she'd eat some sand.
At meals, she'd swallow prune-pits
And never have a pain,
While everyone around her
Would giggle, "Oh Elaine!"

One morning, berry-picking,
A bug was in her pail,
And though we thought for certain
Her appetite would fail,
Elaine said, "Hmm, a stinkbug."
And while we murmured, "Ooh,"
She ate her pail of berries
And ate the stinkbug, too.

Pictures by Marie-Louise Gay

The night of Final Banquet
When counselors were handing
Awards to different children
Whom they believed outstanding,
To every *thinking* person
At summer camp in Maine
The Most Outstanding Camper
Was Eat-it-all Elaine.

BOOKSHELF

Alexander, Who Used to Be Rich Last Sunday by Judith Viorst. Atheneum, 1978. Alexander can't save money like his brothers and he can't remember what happens to the money he gets.

Always Room for One More by Sorche Nic Leodhas. Holt, Rinehart & Winston, 1965. A man with ten children takes in so many travelers that his house falls down.

The Adventures of Spider retold by Joyce Cooper Arkhurst. Little, Brown, 1964. "How Spider Got a Thin Waist" and the other stories in this book tell about the adventures of clever Spider.

Five Sparrows: A Japanese Folktale adapted by Patricia Montgomery Newton. Atheneum, 1982. A Japanese woman helps a hurt sparrow. She is rewarded with a gift of a seed that produces an unending supply of rice.

The Stars in the Sky by Joseph Jacobs. Farrar, Straus & Giroux, 1979. A young girl dreams about wanting stars as toys.

6 There Is a Season...

The Twelve Months

A Russian folk tale retold by Moura Budberg and
Amabel Williams-Ellis
Pictures by Kinuko Craft

Do you know how many months there are in
a year?

Twelve.

What are they?

January, February, March, April, May, June,
July, August, September, October, November,
December.

As soon as one month ends, the next one
begins. February has never once, not once, come
before January, or May before April.

One follows the other, and they never meet.

But people say that in the hilly country of
Bohemia there was a little girl who once saw all
the twelve months at the same time.

How did that come about?

It came about this way.

In a small village there lived a wicked woman who had a daughter and a stepdaughter. She loved her daughter, but the stepdaughter could do nothing to please her. Whatever she did was wrong. Whichever way she turned it was in the wrong direction.

The daughter lay in bed the whole day long eating gingerbread. But the stepdaughter worked from morning till night—fetching water or carrying wood from the forest, or washing linen in the river, or weeding in the orchard.

She felt the bitter cold of the winter, the broiling heat of the summer, the fresh winds of spring, and the autumn rains. Perhaps that is why she managed to see all the twelve months at the same time.

It was winter, the middle of January. There was so much snow that it had to be cleared away from the doors. And in the forest, trees stood up to their waists in snowdrifts and couldn't even sway when the wind pushed them.

People kept indoors and sat by their stoves.

On such a day, towards nightfall, the wicked stepmother opened the door and saw the snowstorm raging. Then she returned to the warm fire and said to her stepdaughter, "You ought to go to the forest and pick some snowdrops. Tomorrow is your sister's birthday."

The little girl glanced at her stepmother. Was she joking, or was she really sending her into the forest? It would be terrifying to go to the forest in weather like this. And what snowdrops could there be in the middle of winter? They never appeared before March, no matter where you looked for them. It would be easy to get lost in the forest, or to sink in the snowdrifts.

Her stepsister said to her, "Even if you do get lost, who is there to worry about you? Go, and don't come back without the flowers. Here, take the basket."

The girl burst into tears. But she wrapped herself in a torn shawl and left the house. The wind tore at the shawl and threw snowflakes into her eyes as she walked through the snowdrifts.

It grew darker and darker. The sky was
black, and there was not a single star to peer
down at the white earth below.

She came to the forest. Now it was quite
dark, and she couldn't even see her hands. The
girl sat on the stump of a tree. If she must freeze
to death, what difference would it make where
she waited?

Suddenly a light flashed far away among the
trees—as if a star had got caught among the
branches.

The girl stood up again and began to struggle towards the light. Often she sank in the snow. Often she had to climb over fallen trees. I mustn't lose the light, she kept thinking to herself. The light became brighter and still brighter. Now she could catch the scent of warm smoke. She could hear the crackling of logs burning in a fire.

On she hurried and soon she came to a clearing in the forest. And here she stood stock still, for it was suddenly very bright as if the sun were shining. There was a huge bonfire burning in the middle of the clearing, with flames reaching almost to the sky. And there were people, some near the bonfire, some farther away. They were talking quietly among themselves.

The girl looked at them and wondered who they could be. They didn't look like hunters and certainly not like woodcutters—they were so beautifully dressed, some in silver, some in gold, some in green velvet.

She began to count and she counted twelve: three old people, three middle-aged, three young ones, and the last three were just boys.

The young ones sat close by the fire, the older ones farther away.

Suddenly one old man turned round—the tallest one, with a long beard and bushy eyebrows—and saw the girl. She was frightened and wanted to run but it was too late. The old man asked her loudly, "Where did you come from? What do you want?"

The little girl showed her empty basket and said, "I've got to pick some snowdrops and put them in my basket."

The old man laughed. "Snowdrops in January! What an idea!"

"It's not my idea," the girl replied. "My stepmother sent me here for them and told me not to come back with an empty basket."

The twelve men glanced at her then and began to whisper among themselves. The girl stood there listening, but she could not make out what they were saying. It was as though it were not people speaking at all, but the trees rustling.

They whispered and whispered and then they stopped.

The tall old man turned to her again and asked, "What will you do if you don't find the snowdrops? They won't appear before March, you know."

"I must stay in the forest," answered the girl. "I'll wait for March. It would be better to freeze to death in the woods than to go home without the snowdrops."

She said this and burst into tears.

Suddenly the youngest of the twelve rose to his feet and walked up to the old man.

"Brother January," he said, "let me come in your place for an hour."

The old man stroked his long beard and said, "I would do it willingly, but March can't come before February."

"It's all right," murmured another old man, very shaggy, with an untidy beard. "You can let him come in your place for an hour. I won't argue! We all of us know this child. We've seen her sometimes at the river with her pails, or in the forest gathering a handful of wood. She's one of us. She belongs to all of us, to all the months, so we must help her now."

"So be it," said old January.

He struck his ice-ax and said:

> "Frosts keep away
>
> From the trees in the forest,
>
> Leave the core
>
> Of the birch, or the pine.
>
> Freeze neither the ravens
>
> Nor houses of men!"

He fell silent and silence came to the forest too. The trees stopped crackling and the snow fell in large, soft flakes.

"Now it's your turn, friend," said January, and handed the ax to his younger brother, shaggy February.

He struck his ax again, shook his beard and howled:

"Winds, gales, storms,
Blow as hard as you can,
Rage the whole night long.
Whistle in the chimneys,
Drum in the skies,
Twist and turn over the earth
Like a great white snake."

And as soon as he had said this a wet, stormy wind began to blow and shook the branches. The snowflakes whirled and whirled and raced over the earth. February handed his ax to his younger brother and said, "Your turn, brother March."

March hit the ground with his ax.

The girl stared and saw that it wasn't an ax any longer; it was a large branch, covered with buds.

March threw back his head and laughed, and began to sing loudly in his clear, young voice:

"Streams, flow merrily,
Pools, overflow,
Come out, little ants
And warm yourselves
After winter's chill.
The bear is leaving his lair
And strolls in the forest;
The birds are singing
And the snowdrops are pushing
        through the earth."

The little girl clapped her hands in surprise. Where had the snowdrifts gone to? Where were the icicles hanging from every branch?

There was soft, fresh earth beneath her feet. All round her she heard the ripple of running water, and the sound of melting snow. The buds on the branches were bursting and green leaves pushed out of their dark skins.

The girl could hardly believe her eyes.

"You mustn't stand and stare," said March to her. "You must hurry, for we have only an hour to do what we want!"

So the little girl stopped staring and rushed into the forest to search for snowdrops—and there were thousands of them! Under the bushes, under the stones, here, there, and everywhere she looked. She picked a whole basketful, filled her apron too, and hurried back to the clearing where the twelve brothers had sat round the fire.

But there was no more fire, and the brothers were gone. It was very light in the clearing, but now it was a different light—not from the fire, but from the full moon that had appeared above the forest trees.

She was sorry she had no one to thank, but as there was nothing else to do she ran off home. The moon lighted her way. She scarcely felt her feet under her until she reached the door. But she hardly had time to walk in before the snowstorm raged again and the moon vanished behind the clouds.

"Ah, so you're back already!" said her stepmother and sister. "Where are the snowdrops?"

The girl didn't reply but poured the snowdrops from her apron onto the bench and put the basket beside them.

The stepmother and sister were amazed.

"Where did you get them?"

The girl told them all that had happened. They listened and shook their heads, not knowing whether to believe her or not. It was hard to believe, but there were the snowdrops, all fresh and white, lying on the bench to remind one of March.

357

They exchanged sidelong glances, and the stepmother asked:

"Did the months give you anything else?"

"I didn't ask them for anything else."

"What a fool, what a fool!" said her stepsister. "To think that you met all twelve months at once and did not ask them for anything but snowdrops. Had I been in your place, I would have known what to ask for. I'd have asked one for apples and sweet pears, the other for ripe strawberries, the third for tasty mushrooms, the fourth for fresh cucumbers."

"There's a clever girl!" said the stepmother. "In the winter, strawberries and pears are beyond price. We might have sold them and for so much money! And this little fool brings nothing but snowdrops! Put on some warm clothes, my daughter, and go to the clearing. They won't pull the wool over *your* eyes, though there are twelve of them to your one."

"They certainly won't!" answered her daughter, her arms already in her sleeves and a kerchief over her head.

Her mother shouted after her, "Put on mittens, and button up your coat."

But the door had already closed behind her. She ran to the forest, following her sister's footsteps.

The sooner I get to the clearing, the better, she thought.

The forest was dense and dark, the snowdrifts high, rising like a wall.

Oh! thought the girl. Why on earth did I choose to come to the forest, instead of staying in my warm bed? I'm frozen to the bone and am sure to catch my death of cold!

Hardly were the words out of her mouth before she caught sight of a light in the distance—as if a star had got caught in the branches.

She went towards the light, struggling
through the snow, and finally came to the
clearing. A large woodpile was burning there and
around it sat the twelve months, softly talking to
one another.

She walked up to the fire. She did not bow
in greeting or say a kind word, but chose the best
spot and sat down to get warm.

The brothers fell silent. The forest was still.
Suddenly January struck his ax on the ground.

"Who are you?" he asked. "Where do you
come from?"

"From my house," the girl replied. "You have given my sister a large basket of snowdrops. So I came, following her footsteps."

"We know your sister," said January, "but we've never set eyes on you. What is the purpose of your visit?"

"I've come for presents. I want June to fill my basket with strawberries, and I'd like large ones too. And July could give me fresh cucumbers and white mushrooms, and August some sweet pears and apples. September could give me some ripe nuts. And October . . . "

"Wait a moment," said January. "Summer doesn't come before spring or spring before winter. It's a long way to go yet until the month of June. I'm January, the master of the forest now, and I shall reign here for thirty-one days."

"How disagreeable you are!" said the girl. "It's not you I came to see at all! There's nothing to get from you but snow and frost. It's the summer months I want."

January frowned. "Search for summer in the winter," he said.

He waved his great sleeve and a snowstorm blew up from the earth to the sky covering the trees and the clearing where the twelve brothers were sitting. One could not even see the fire for the snow. One could only hear it hissing somewhere, crackling and moaning.

The girl was suddenly terrified. "Stop!" she cried. "Stop! That's enough!"

But it was all in vain.

The snowstorm was whirling around her, blinding her, and she couldn't breathe. She fell down in a snowdrift and was buried under soft white snow.

The mother waited and waited for her daughter. She peered out of the window and rushed to the door, but there was no sign of her. So she wrapped herself up warmly and went to the forest. But how could she hope to find her child in such a storm! She walked and walked, and searched high and low, but she found nothing.

And so they stayed there, both of them in the forest, to wait for the coming of the summer.

The other girl lived on happily. She grew into a young woman, married, and had children.

And she had a garden round her house. People said that such a wondrous garden had never been seen before. Flowers bloomed there before anywhere else. Berries ripened. Pears and apples mellowed. It was cool in the heat of summer, quiet in a storm.

"All the months of the year seem to visit that young woman at once," people used to say.

And who knows? Perhaps it was the truth.

Questions

1. If you made this story into a play, what two places would your stage show?

2. Why did the Twelve Months treat the two girls differently?

3. In the story the stepmother said to her daughter, "They won't pull the wool over *your* eyes." What did she mean?
   a. They won't cover your face.
   b. They won't fool you.
   c. They won't let you get cold.

4. People have told the story of "The Twelve Months" for many years. Why do you think people might have told this tale again and again? Give two reasons.

Activity   Write the Months and Their Gifts

Fold a piece of paper into sixteen squares. Use the four squares across the top for a title: "Gifts from the Months." Write the name of each month in one of the twelve squares that are left. In each square, draw or write what you hope each month would bring you.

Gifts	from	the	Months
January ✳	February		

CONNECTIONS

The Four Seasons

Spring, summer, fall, winter—each season brings its own beauty. Each brings changes to the world of nature.

Why Do We Have Seasons?

The Earth moves around the Sun. This trip takes a year. Look at the picture on page 367. It shows the Earth as each season begins in the northern half of the planet.

The Earth is tilted as it travels. This tilt causes the seasons. In summer the tilt causes more sunlight to reach the northern half of Earth. As the Earth moves on, less sunlight reaches this half of Earth and it is fall. Look at what happens in winter and spring as the Earth continues to move around the Sun.

Pictures by Keith Freeman

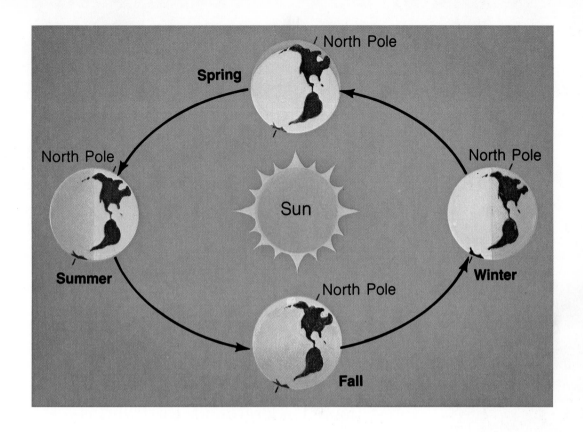

What Changes Do the Seasons Bring?

Each season brings changes to life on
Earth. Such changes are easy to see in a
temperate (TEM·per·it) *forest*. This kind of
forest has many trees that lose their leaves
in the fall. The temperate forest is the
habitat (HAB·uh·tat), or living place, for
many creatures. The forest changes in
many ways as the seasons change.

Spring It is spring in the forest. Sunlight streams through budding branches. It warms the earth. Wildflowers carpet the forest floor. Underground, earthworms tunnel upward, just in time for the return of robins from the south. Everywhere the songs of birds fill the air.

The trees begin to unfold new leaves. Animals and insects awake from a long winter's sleep. Now the animals will begin to shed their winter coats.

Spring is the time for animals to be born. Soon the forest fills with new life. Safe in their nest, these baby squirrels wait for mother to return. They are hungry!

Summer Then summer comes. The forest is hot. It is dark with shade. The animals and birds are quiet. Many of them rest during the day. They come out at night when it is cooler. Summer is the season for insects. They are everywhere, searching for food. Some find it in the trees, where they chew the leaves and rob the trees of sap.

The young squirrels are growing. The older squirrels are still shedding their long hairs. Their tails look thin and ragged. Soon they will begin to grow thick winter coats.

Fall The days are getting shorter and cooler. It is fall. The trees blaze with color. The forest is lit with red, gold, and bright orange. The trees drop their seeds on the forest floor—acorns, beechnuts, hickory nuts, butternuts. These are taken away by birds and animals, to be stored as winter food.

Raccoons and bears eat greedily. They make themselves fat. They will live off this fat in the winter, when food is scarce. Flocks of birds circle overhead. They begin their long flight south.

To prepare for winter, the squirrels now have thick fur coats and bushy tails. They are busy hiding nuts. They bury bushels of nuts over the forest floor. Some nuts will be dug up and eaten. Others will be forgotten, and some will sprout and grow up to be trees.

Winter Fall ends and winter begins. The trees have lost their leaves, and cold snow blankets their branches. Deer search for tender twigs not covered by the snow. Foxes look for rabbits.

Brown bears are curled up, asleep in their caves. Many animals *hibernate* (HY·buhr·NAYT), or spend the winter in a still, quiet state that is almost like sleeping. Below ground, toads, snakes, turtles, and chipmunks hibernate in holes they have made. Insects hibernate, too, protected from the cold by leaves and earth. Other insects have died, but they have left eggs that will hatch in the spring.

On warm winter days the squirrels scamper about looking for food. On cold days they find a hollow tree or nest of leaves and sleep.

The whole forest seems to wait. Soon spring will come, and the circle of the seasons will continue again.

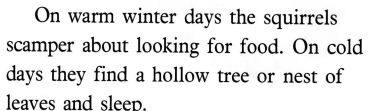

Questions

1. Look at the picture on page 367. When the northern half of the Earth is tilted away from the Sun, what season is it?

2. In a temperate forest, how does an oak tree change in spring? in summer? in fall? in winter?

3. Brown bears sleep in the winter, but toads hibernate. What is the difference between sleep and hibernation?

Activity   Write a Season Poem

Write a poem about a season. First choose a season. Then list your favorite things for that season. You could write your list like the one shown in the picture. For different ways to write poems, read again the poems on pages 374 to 381 in your book.

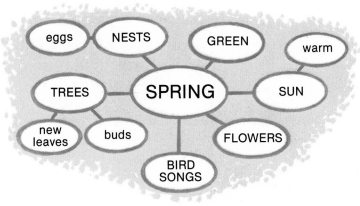

Winter Night

A poem by Harry Behn

It is very dark
But not late.
Not after eight.

The only light
Comes from snow
Beginning to show.

Bushes are first
As flakes fall,
Then the top of a wall.

What used to be dark
Is now a hill.
It is very still.

Picture by Christa Kieffer

A very fat snowman named Wheezer
Was truly a clever old geezer.
   Whenever he felt
   He was starting to melt,
He'd spend a few days in the freezer.

A limerick by Edward Mullins

Picture by Ed Taber

Winter Walk

A poem by Robert Froman

Cold sky, cold air, cold sidewalk, cold street.

Cold.

SHIVERS.

GOOSE pimples.

RUUUBBB HAAANDDDS.

STAMP FEET.

STILL COLD.

GO IN THIS STORE A MINUTE.

AHHHHHHHHH!

Picture by Christa Kieffer

In Time of Silver Rain

A poem by Langston Hughes

In time of silver rain
The earth
Puts forth new life again,
Green grasses grow
And flowers lift their heads,
And over all the plain
The wonder spreads
Of life, of life, of life!

March

A poem by Elizabeth Coatsworth

A blue day,
a blue jay
and a good beginning.

One crow
melting snow—
spring's winning!

376

Spring

A poem by Karla Kuskin

I'm shouting
I'm singing
I'm swinging through trees
I'm winging skyhigh
With the buzzing black bees.
I'm the sun
I'm the moon
I'm the dew on the rose.
I'm a rabbit
Whose habit
Is twitching his nose.
I'm lively
I'm lovely
I'm kicking my heels.
I'm crying "Come dance"
To the fresh water eels.
I'm racing through meadows
Without any coat
I'm a gamboling lamb
I'm a light leaping goat.
I'm a bud
I'm a bloom
I'm a dove on the wing.
I'm running on rooftops
And welcoming spring!

Picture by Christa Kieffer

The Fourth of July

A poem by Myra Cohn Livingston

O say
can you
see
in the sky
the rockets
and
pinwheels
zip
by
to
splutter
and flare
as they
sizzle
in
air
and
EXPLODE
on
the Fourth
of
July!

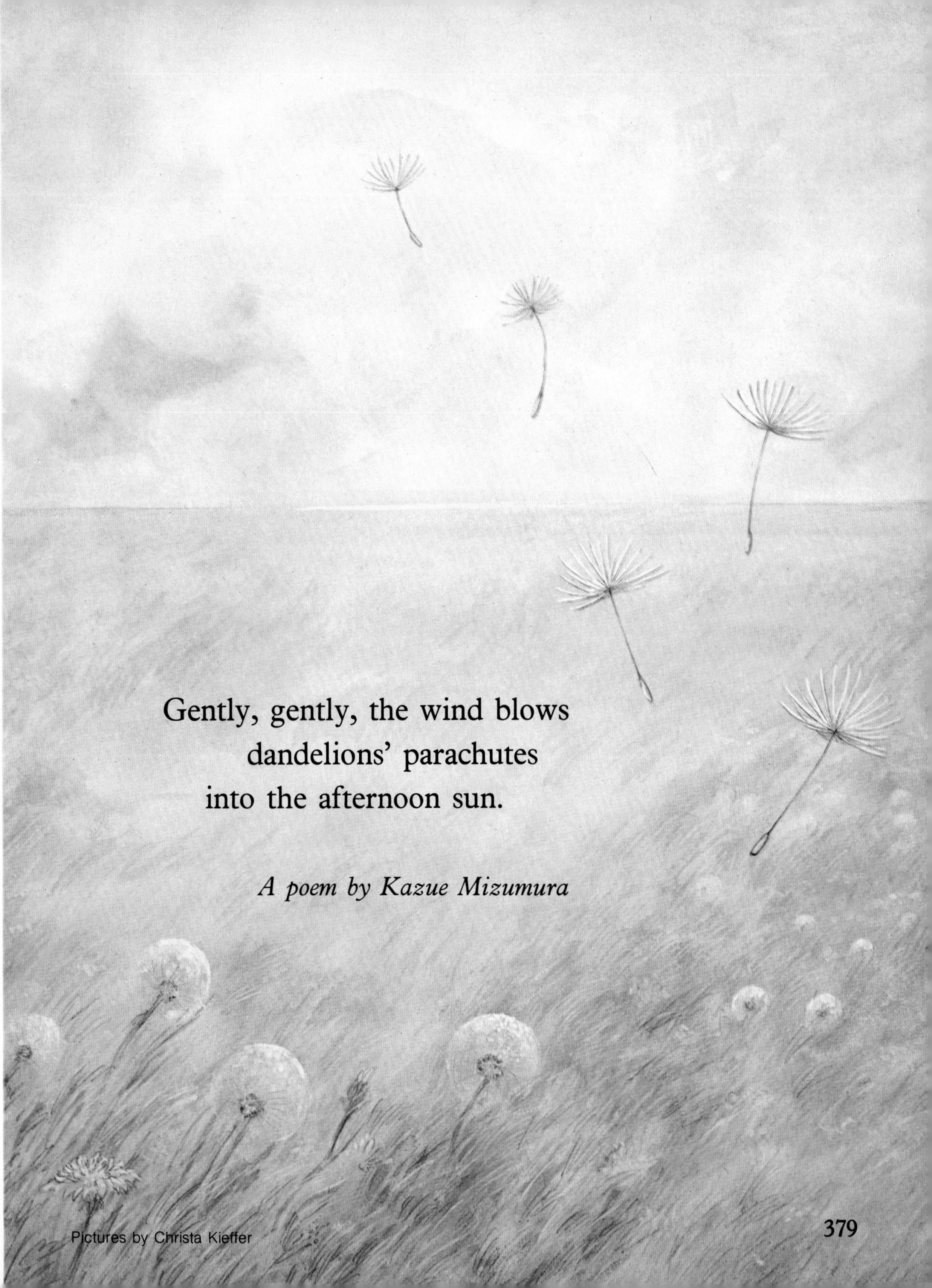

Gently, gently, the wind blows
dandelions' parachutes
into the afternoon sun.

A poem by Kazue Mizumura

Pictures by Christa Kieffer

Fall

A haiku by Sally Andresen

The geese flying south
In a row long and V-shaped
Pulling in winter.

Spendthrift

A poem by Norma Farber

Coins—coins—coins—
     a bushel to a breeze—
are pouring from the pockets
     of the elm in the square.

Gather up the money heaps
     as many as you please.
So rich an old tree
     doesn't count them or care.

Theme in Yellow

A poem by Carl Sandburg

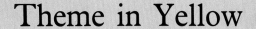

I spot the hills
With yellow balls in autumn.
I light the prairie cornfields
Orange and tawny gold clusters
And I am called pumpkins.
On the last of October
When dusk is fallen
Children join hands
And circle round me
Singing ghost songs
And love to the harvest moon;
I am a jack-o'-lantern
With terrible teeth
And the children know
I am fooling.

Pictures by Christa Kieffer

Panda

A story by Susan Bonners
Pictures by Tom Dunnington

In a mountain forest of southwestern
China, a giant panda sits in a birch tree.
Snowflakes fall on her black and white fur,
but she does not look for shelter. She has
lived in snow most of her life.

Early one autumn, the panda found a
den in a rocky mountainside. There she
made a nest out of broken bamboo stalks.
While frosty winds blew through the forest,
she gave birth to her cub.

The panda cub was so tiny, she could easily be covered by one of her mother's paws. The cub weighed only five ounces. She was smaller than a kitten, but she had a loud voice that sounded like a baby's cry.

The cub had just a thin covering of white fur. Only her mother's warmth kept her alive. Day and night, the mother panda held her cub tightly against her large, warm body. She never put her cub down.

For several days, the mother panda stayed in the den and nursed her cub. Eventually, the mother had to eat. Carefully, she looked outside. She sniffed the chilly air. She listened to the sounds of the forest. Then, carrying her cub in one paw, the mother panda left the den. She did not have far to go for food. Still cradling her cub, she ate some of the bamboo that grew all around her.

Soon the panda cub began to look like her mother. By the time the cub was one-month old, she had a soft, thick coat of black and white fur. She could not crawl yet, but she could roll around a little.

Now the mother panda could leave her cub for a short time. Before the mother left, she always put her cub in a hidden place. At the cub's first cry, the mother hurried back to soothe her cub by stroking her with a paw.

The cub grew quickly. At two months, she weighed seven pounds, twenty times more than when she was born. Her voice was softer now, a kind of bleating sound. The mother panda played with the cub, tossing her gently between her paws.

All this time, the cub's eyes had been closed. She lived in a world of sounds and smells. She could hear her mother's heart beating. She could smell her mother and feel her warmth, but she could not see her.

At two-and-a-half months, the cub's eyes opened, and she began to see the world around her. She saw bamboo growing in tall thickets that stayed green all winter. There were spruce, birch, and maple trees. Sometimes, a golden monkey swung on the branches. Birds flew overhead—the titmouse, the nuthatch, and the laughing thrush.

At three months, the cub was able to crawl. Now she could explore the world on her own. Often, while her mother slept, the cub sniffed over everything she could find. The cub did not spend all her time exploring, though. Sometimes, she just played.

In the spring, the cub was five months
old and still lived on her mother's milk.
She weighed twenty pounds.

One day, while her mother was eating
bamboo, the cub nibbled a bamboo leaf.
She crunched a thin bamboo shoot with her
milk teeth. As her jaws became stronger,
she ate bigger and bigger stalks.

Her mother could eat woody stalks of
bamboo an inch-and-a-half thick. The
mother liked to eat some leaves first.
Holding the stalk, she let herself fall slowly
backwards.

The mother panda ate twenty pounds
of bamboo every day. Giant pandas have
special linings in their throats and stomachs
to protect them. They can even swallow
splinters without being hurt.

Summer came. To escape the heat, the cub and her mother went up to the cool meadows above the forest. In the meadows, they ate irises and crocuses, vines, and tufted grasses. A panda has a special bone in its wrist that works like a thumb, so it can pick things up with a very delicate grasp.

Now the panda cub was able to take care of herself, but she stayed with her mother a while longer. The cub kept growing and getting stronger. When she was a year old, she weighed eighty pounds. Her coat became wiry. She lost her milk teeth and grew large permanent teeth.

Then the cub went off to live on her own.

Questions

1. What is the most important plant for a giant panda? Why?

2. When the baby panda was tiny, what kind of voice did she have? How did it help?

3. "Panda" tells facts about a panda's life. How would "Panda" be different if it were a make-believe story?

4. Match each word with its meaning.
   a. bamboo   a flower
   b. nuthatch   a green plant
   c. iris   a bird

Activity   Make a Time Line

Make a time line for the giant panda. The time line begins when she is born. It ends when she is one year old. On your time line, show these times in order: one month, two months, two-and-a-half months, three months. Write a sentence about each age.

Save the Animals

For a long time giant pandas have lived on cool mountainsides in China. The mountain forests give them shelter and plenty of bamboo, the special food they need to live.

Many people also live in China, and they must have food, too. So mountainsides that were homes for pandas were turned into farmland. Bamboo forests that were the panda's food were cut down.

With fewer forests, there was not enough room or food for all the pandas. Some pandas starved. Fewer panda babies were born. Time passed, and fewer and fewer pandas survived.

Pictures by Tom Dunnington

Then the giant pandas met a new problem. The bamboo forests began to die!

A bamboo plant dies after it grows flowers and produces seeds. The seeds grow into new plants, but it takes at least three years before the bamboo plants are big enough for pandas to eat.

During the time it takes for bamboo plants to grow big, pandas can starve. So people in China and other countries decided to help. Many people gave money for "Project Panda." Rescue teams brought the starving pandas to places where they could be fed and cared for. These pandas were moved to a *preserve* (prih·ZURV), an area planted with bamboo where the pandas would be safe. All over the world people began to study pandas and to seek ways to help the pandas survive.

Yet giant pandas are only one kind of animal that is in danger of dying off. There are many other *endangered animals*. People are trying to save these animals, too.

Questions

1. What is one reason that pandas are endangered?

2. What does it mean to be *endangered*? Be a panda and answer this question.

Activity   Prepare an Animal Report

Choose one of the animals pictured on these pages. Find out what it eats. Find out why it is endangered. Find out what people are doing to save it. Then write or give a report to share what you have learned with others.

ENDANGERED! California condor
California

ENDANGERED! Whooping crane
Canada and Texas

ENDANGERED! Sea otter
West Coast of the United States

ENDANGERED! Gorilla
West Africa

ENDANGERED! Siberian tiger
Mountains of China, Korea,
eastern Russia

ENDANGERED!
Galapagos giant tortoise
Galapagos islands

ENDANGERED! Bald eagle
United States and Canada

ENDANGERED! Key deer
Florida Keys

From

Along Sandy Trails

A story by Ann Nolan Clark
Photographs by Alfred A. Cohn

My grandmother tells me,
  "Small Papago Indian,
  girl of the Desert People,
  for two summer moons
  I will walk with you
  across the sand patches,
  by the rock ridges
  and the cacti,
  through the dry washes
  and along the sandy trails
  that you may know the desert
  and hold its beauty
  in your heart forever."

I walk with my grandmother
   along a sandy trail.
The sand beneath my feet
   is damp and cool
   because, last night
   while I was sleeping,
   clouds rained down
   upon our thirsty land.

Rain washed the flowers
   of all the cacti,
   the pincushion
   and the cholla
   (CHOH·yah),
   the hedgehog
   and the prickly pear.

We sit by the trail to rest.
Beside me a lizard's track
   is penciled lightly
   on the sand.
I touch it with my fingers.
I see a gila (HEE•lah) woodpecker
   pecking the trunk
   of a giant cactus.
If I listen . . . listen . . . listen,
   I will hear him pecking.

Along the trail
   a roadrunner runs
   all stretched out
   as if he cannot get
   to where he is going
   fast enough, soon enough.
I look and see. I listen and hear.
There are so many things
   in this quiet land.

But I like best the quail.
I watch them walking,
    their black plumes bobbing
    from their red bonnets.
They walk across the trail
    near my grandmother and me,
    so busy talking together
    they do not see us.

Quail do not hop
    as some birds do.
They walk elegantly
    with quick, small steps.
Other birds walk alone,
    but quail go everywhere
    with their families
    and their friends.
They go in coveys.

Then my grandmother says,
    "Down the trail a little distance
    I will show you something
    to remember always."
We walk along and come
    to a spreading creosote.

Under its branches, on the ground,
    in a round place
    lined with desert grass,
    is a quail's nest.
In the nest are many eggs.
One is broken.
I count them
    but do not touch them
    or make a noise of any kind.

My grandmother whispers,
    "Watch. Be still.
    See the guard quail
    sitting on the cholla,
    not eating,
    not talking,
    just sitting.
    Listen. If he calls
    cra-er, cra-er, cra-er,
    he is warning his covey
    of danger."

I like best the quail.
But my grandmother likes
    the giant cactus,
    standing tall and stark
    against the sky.
Giant cactus gives us
    many important things.
The rain water stored
    in its pleated trunk
    stays our thirst
    when the winds
    of the dry moon
    sweep across our land.
Its white and yellow flower-crowns
    ripen slowly to scarlet fruit
    that we gather
    and store as food
    for the time
    of the hunger moon.

Our baskets are filled
    with the ripe fruit
    of the giant cactus
    that we have gathered,
    my grandmother and I,
    and that now we take
    to my mother's house.
The sand beneath our feet
    is deep and shifting.
The way seems long
    and our baskets are heavy.
We walk and rest.
We walk and rest.
After a time of just resting,
    happy and quiet,
    Grandmother says, "Come,
    little granddaughter.
    The sun travels westward
    to make the day's ending.
    Your father has worked
    his fields.
    Your mother has woven
    her baskets.
    Nighttime is waiting."

Questions

1. Why did the grandmother and her granddaughter walk in the desert?

2. What are three ways in which the quail are different from most other birds?

3. Suppose someone said, "The desert is nothing but dry sand." What might the girl in the story reply?

4. The girl talks about the giant cactus and the hunger moon. What is the hunger moon?
   a. a moon that is hungry
   b. a time when people might be hungry
   c. a time when the moon looks empty

5. Why do you think this story has the title *Along Sandy Trails?*

Activity   Make a Map

Trails are everywhere. They may be sidewalk trails or road trails or park trails. Make a map of a trail near your home. Draw arrows to show the path to follow. Draw and label pictures of things to see along your trail.

I Go Forth to Move About the Earth

A poem by Alonzo Lopez

I go forth to move about the earth.
I go forth as the owl, wise and knowing.
I go forth as the eagle, powerful and bold.
I go forth as the dove, peaceful and gentle.
I go forth to move about the earth
    in wisdom, courage, and peace.

405

BOOKSHELF

Old Sadie and the Christmas Bear by Phyllis Reynolds Naylor. Atheneum, 1984. A bear, instead of sleeping through the winter, wakes to take a walk at Christmas. He visits a lady and makes her holiday a special one.

The Boy Who Didn't Believe in Spring by Lucille Clifton. E. P. Dutton, 1973. King Shabazz doesn't believe it when adults tell him that "spring is just around the corner." So he and his friend Tony set out to find spring, wherever it may be.

Ox-Cart Man by Donald Hall and illustrated by Barbara Cooney. Penguin, 1979. This story follows a New England farmer in the 1800s from the time he sells his goods and belongings to the time he and his family start the cycle of making and growing things all over again.

Little Wild Lion Cub by Anna Michel. Pantheon, 1980. Soft drawings show an active little cub and his family during the first two years of his life.

GLOSSARY

This glossary gives the meanings of unfamiliar words used in the text of this book. The meanings given here define words only the way they are used in the book. You can find other meanings for these words in a dictionary.

The correct pronunciation of each glossary word is given in the special spelling after that word. The sounds used in these spellings are explained in the following Pronunciation Key. Each symbol, or letter, stands for a sound, a sound you can recognize in the words following it. In addition to these sounds, each glossary pronunciation includes marks to show the kind of force, or stress, with which certain syllables are pronounced. A heavy mark, ′, shows that the syllable it follows is given the strongest, or primary, stress, as in **sis·ter** (sis′·ter). A lighter mark, ′, shows that the syllable it follows is given a secondary, or lighter, stress, as in **tax·i·cab** (tak′·sē·kab′).

Several abbreviations are used in the glossary: *v.,* verb; *n.,* noun; *adj.,* adjective; *pl.,* plural.

Pronunciation Key

a	add, map	m	move, seem	u	up, done
ā	ace, rate	n	nice, tin	û(r)	urn, term
â(r)	care, air	ng	ring, song	yōo	use, few
ä	palm, father	o	odd, hot	v	vain, eve
b	bat, rub	ō	open, so	w	win, away
ch	check, catch	ô	order, jaw	y	yet, yearn
d	dog, rod	oi	oil, boy	z	zest, muse
e	end, pet	ou	out, now	zh	vision, pleasure
ē	even, tree	ōo	pool, food	ə	the schwa,
f	fit, half	o͝o	took, full		an unstressed
g	go, log	p	pit, stop		vowel representing
h	hope, hate	r	run, poor		the sound spelled
i	it, give	s	see, pass		a in above
ī	ice, write	sh	sure, rush		e in sicken
j	joy, ledge	t	talk, sit		i in possible
k	cook, take	th	thin, both		o in melon
l	look, rule	th	this, bathe		u in circus

a·ca·cia (ə·kā′·shə) *n.* A tree with fronds and yellow flowers that grows in warm places.

ac·cept (ak·sept′) *v.* To take something that someone gives.

ap·pli·ca·tion (ap′·lə·kā′·shən) *n.* A form one fills in with personal information when asking for something.

ar·a·besque (ar′·ə·besk′) *n.* A position in ballet in which the body bends forward at the hip, and one arm and leg are forward while the other arm and leg extend backward.

a·rach·nid (ə·rak′·nid) *n.* A class of animals without a backbone and having four pairs of legs and a body divided into two parts. Spiders, scorpions, mites, and ticks are *arachnids.*

ar·mored (är′·mərd) *adj.* Having a covering like armor, a strong protective suit worn in battles.

ball (bôl) *n.* A dance.

bal·let (ba·lā′) *n.* A kind of dancing that combines certain steps with light, flowing movements such as leaps and turns. Ballet dancers wear special costumes. Some wear toe shoes to help them dance on their toes.

bam·boo (bam·bōō′) *n.* Woody grasses with hollow stems used for buildings, furniture, and tools. The young shoots are used for food.

barbed wire (bärbd wīr) *n.* Twisted wires with sharp points every few inches.

bar·ri·cade (bar′·ə·kād′) *n.* Something used to block off an entrance.

bay (bā) *v.* To bark with a drawn-out howl.

beau·te·ous (byōōt′·ē·əs) *adj.* Beautiful; pleasing.

bee·tle (bēt′·əl) *n.* An insect with four wings, one pair of which forms a hard shell and covers the other pair when not flying.

bleat·ing (blēt′·ing) *adj.* Crying like a sheep or a goat.

bon·fire (bon′·fīr) *n.* A fire made from stacks of burning logs.

bon·y (bō′·nē) *adj.* Made of bone.

bound·a·ry (boun′·də·rē) *n.* A border or separating line.

brew (brōō) *n.* A kind of drink.

bulg·ing (bəlj′·ing) *adj.* Swelling.

cac·ti (kak′·tī) *n., pl.* Desert plants with thick stems and spines.

calm (käm) *adj.* Peaceful.

Ca·na·di·an (kə·nā′·dē·ən) *adj.* A native of Canada, a country north of the United States.

car·go (kär′·gō) *n.* Goods brought on ships, airplanes, and trucks.

cav·ern·ous (kav′·ər·nəs) *adj.*
Having a deep, hollow area like
a cave.

char·ac·ter (kar′·ik·tər) *n.* A person
or an animal in a play.

chat·ter (chat′·ər) *v.* To make fast
clicking noises.

Chi·na (chī′·nə) *n.* A country on the
continent of Asia.

chirp (chûrp) *v.* To make a short,
sharp sound.

clay (klā) *n.* Earth or mud that can
be used for bricks or pottery.

com·mu·ni·ty (kə·myoo′·nə·tē) *n.*
A people with common interests
living in a certain area.

com·pu·ter (kəm·pyoo′·tər) *n.* An
electronic device that can store,
get back, and use information.

con·fi·dent·ly (kon′·fə·dənt·lē) *adv.*
Feeling good about oneself.

con·trap·tion (kən·trap′·shən) *n.*
A gadget; a thing built in an
unusual way.

cov·ey (kəv′·ē) *n.* A small flock of
birds.

crav·ing (krāv′·ing) *n.* A desire.

cre·o·sote (krē′·ə·sōt′) *n.* A desert
shrub found in the southwestern
United States.

cringe (krinj) *v.* To draw away
from in horror.

croc·o·dile (krok′·ə·dīl′) *n.* A large,
thick-skinned reptile that lives in
warm, tropical waters.

cus·tom·er (kəs′·tə·mər) *n.* A
person who buys goods or
services.

cy·clone (sī′·klōn) *n.* A whirlwind; a
storm that brings rain and high
winds that go around in a circle.

del·i·cate (del′·ə·kit) *adj.* Easily
harmed; finely skilled.

den (den) *n.* A cave used by a
wild animal as a living area.

de·serve (di·zûrv′) *v.* To be worthy
of having a reward.

dis·a·gree·a·ble (dis′·ə·grē′·ə·bəl)
adj. Not pleasing.

dis·guise (dis·gīz′) *v.* To hide one's
true appearance by putting on a
covering or clothes.

ditch (dich) *n.* A long narrow hole
dug in the ground and used for
draining land or for bringing
water to plants.

drag·on (drag′·ən) *n.* An imaginary
animal usually shown with a
snake-like tail, huge wings, and
claws.

e·lec·tric·i·ty (i·lek′·tris′·ə·tē) *n.*
Electric current that runs
machines.

em·per·or (em′pər·ər) *n.* A ruler of
an empire.

en·core (än′·kôr) *n.* A request by
an audience for a repeat
performance.

en·dan·gered (in·dān′·jərd) *adj.*
Threatened with loss of life.

es·cape (ə·skāp′) *n.* The act of
getting away.

ex·pen·sive (ik·spen′·siv) *adj.*
Costing a great deal.

ex·plore (ik·splôr′) *v.* To search.

ex·plor·er (ik·splôr′·ər) *n.* A person
who travels to new places to
learn about the land.

fac·to·ry (fak′·tə·rē) *n.* A building
where goods are made.

flock (flok) *n.* A group of birds.

flood (flud) *v.* To cover or fill with
a great deal of water, usually
over land not already covered
with water.

ford (fôrd) *n.* A shallow part of a
river or other body of water
where people can go across.

fu·el (fyoo′·əl) *n.* Material used to
make heat or power by burning.

gale (gāl) *n.* A strong wind.

gam·bol·ing (gam′·bəl·ing) *adj.*
Skipping about in play.

ga·zelle (gə·zel′) *n.* A small, quick,
and graceful African antelope.

geese (gēs) *n., pl.* Large birds with
long necks that live near bodies
of water and that are between
swans and ducks in size.

gra·cious (grā′·shəs) *adj.* Full of
kindness and courtesy.

grasp (grasp) *v.* To take and hold
tightly or firmly.

greed·i·ly (grēd′·ə·lē) *adv.* Wanting
all that one can get.

Greek (grēk) *n.* A person from
Greece, a country in Europe.

guin·ea pig (gin′·ē pig) *n.* A small,
round-bodied, short-eared
animal that is nearly tailless.

hab·i·tat (hab′·ə·tat′) *n.* The place
where an animal or a plant
usually lives and grows.

har·vest (här′·vəst) *n.* The
gathering in of food crops.

hatch (hach) *v.* To come out of
an egg.

hi·ber·nate (hī′·bər·nāt′) *v.* To
spend the winter in a resting
and less active state.

hives (hīvz) *n.* A skin disease in
which the skin itches and
shows patches of red.

hoarse·ly (hôrs′·lē) *adv.* Making a
rough or harsh sound.

hol·low (hol′·ō) *adj.* Empty on the
inside.

hur·ri·cane (hər′·ə·kān′) *n.* A
serious storm with heavy rains
and strong winds that move in a
circle at high speeds.

hur·tle (hər′·təl) *v.* To move with
great speed or force.

hutch (həch) *n.* An animal pen.

In·di·a (in′·dē·ə) *n.* A country in
southern Asia.

410

in·hab·i·tant (in·hab′·ə·tənt) *n.* A person or an animal that lives in a particular place.

in·sect (in′·sekt) *n.* A small animal with three body parts, three pairs of legs, and often two pairs of wings.

in·va·sion (in·vā′·zhən) *n.* The act of entering to attack and conquer.

in·vis·i·ble (in·viz′·ə·bəl) *adj.* Not able to be seen.

in·vite (in·vīt′) *v.* To politely ask someone to do something.

jo·ta (hō′·ta) *n.* A Spanish dance.

jug·gle (jəg′·əl) *v.* To keep several things in the air by tossing and catching them.

la·bor (lā′·bər) *n.* Work.

lad·ing (lā′·ding) *n.* A cargo or load.

lair (lâr) *n.* A place where a wild animal sleeps.

lev·ee (lev′·ē) *n.* A bank or wall that prevents flooding.

lin·ing (lī′·ning) *n.* An inside covering.

li·quid (lik′·wid) *n.* A watery fluid.

lo·co·mo·tive (lō′·kə·mō′·tiv) *n.* The engine of a train.

loy·al·ty (loi′·əl·tē) *n.* The state of being faithful to another person or thing.

ma·de·moi·selle (mad′·ə·mə·zel′) *n.* French for an unmarried woman or girl. It means the same as *Miss*.

mag·ni·fy·ing glass (mag′·nə·fī′·ing glas) *n.* A lens that makes things appear larger than they are.

mam·mal (mam′·əl) *n.* The highest class of animals, including humans and animals that have skin usually covered by hair.

man·gy (mān′·jē) *adj.* Shabby; dirty.

marshy (mär′·shē) *adj.* Like a marsh; having soft wet land.

ma·zur·ka (mə·zər′·kə) *n.* A Polish folk dance.

mes·sen·ger (mes′·ən·jər) *n.* A person who goes on errands.

me·ter (mē′·tər) *n.* A unit of length in the metric system that is equal to 39.37 inches.

mi·gra·tion (mī·grā′·shən) *n.* A yearly trip by an animal from one living place to another.

mil·ler (mil′·ər) *n.* A person who grinds grain into flour.

monk (mungk) *n.* A man who lives in a special religious house called a monastery.

mor·tar (môr′·tər) *n.* A mixture used to seal bricks together.

mur·mur (mər′·mər) *n.* A low unclear sound.

mutt (mət) *n.* A dog of mixed

breeds.

muz·zle (məz′·əl) *n.* The nose and jaws of an animal.

nib·ble (nib′·əl) *v.* To eat or chew in small bites.

o·blig·ing·ly (ə·blī′·jing·lē) *adv.* Willingly.

or·bit (ôr′·bit) *n.* The path of one object around another.

or·ches·tra (ôr′·kəs·trə) *n.* A group of musicians that plays music together.

pal·ace (pal′·əs) *n.* A large, stately house where a king or queen might live.

palp (palp) *n.* A jointed part that helps some animals touch things and taste food.

pan·da (pan′·də) Full name, *giant panda. n.* A large black-and-white animal from China that looks like a bear but is also related to the raccoon family.

Pa·pa·go Indians (pa′·pə·gō) *n.* An American Indian group living in southern Arizona.

par·a·chute (par′·ə·shoot) *n.* Umbrella-shaped material that helps people float to the ground when jumping from an airplane.

peace pipe (pēs pīp) *n.* A decorated pipe that some American Indian groups have used in ceremonies.

pen·guin (peng′·gwin) *n.* A black-and-white bird that does not fly and lives in the Antarctic.

per·ma·nent (pûr′·mə·nənt) *adj.* Not changing.

pest (pest) *n.* A person who annoys another.

phlox (floks) *n.* An American herb with red, purple, white, or mixed colored flowers.

pinch (pinch) *v.* To squeeze between finger and thumb.

plié (plē·ā′) *n.* A ballet step by a dancer who bends the knees but holds the back straight.

pos·sum (pos′·əm) The informal name for **opossum**. *n.* A small animal that usually feeds at night and lives in trees, found in the eastern United States.

prai·rie (prâr′·ē) *n.* A large area of level or rolling grassy land, having few or no trees, especially the plains of the central United States.

pre·serve (pri·zûrv′) *n.* An area where animals are protected.

prod·uct (prod′·əkt) *n.* Something made, produced, or grown, such as farm products.

proj·ect (proj′·ekt) *n.* A large task or job.

pro·tect (prə·tekt′) *v.* To keep from harm.

rage (rāj) v. To show great anger or violence.

rav·en·ous (rav′·ə·nəs) adj. Very hungry.

re·as·sure (rē′·ə·shoŏr′) v. To free from fear or doubt; give confidence.

reck·on (rek′·ən) v. To plan or count on.

rec·re·a·tion (rek′·rē·ā′·shən) n. Play or amusement.

reign (rān) v. To have power over others.

res·cue (res′·kyoō) v. To save from danger, harm, or disaster.

riv·er (riv′·ər) n. A large, natural stream of water; often fed by smaller streams and flowing to a lake or sea.

roast·ing pit (rō′·sting pit) n. A large hole in the ground over which food is cooked.

salve (sav) n. A sticky medicine to put on wounds and sores.

saw·mill (sô′·mil′) n. A place where logs are cut.

scarce (skârs) adj. Not plentiful.

sci·en·tist (sī′·ən·tist) n. A person who studies science.

Scot·land (skot′·lənd) n. A country in Europe north of England and part of the United Kingdom of Great Britain.

sculp·ture (skulp′·chər) n. The art of carving or modeling materials into figures or shapes.

sea·weed (sē′·wēd) n. Plants that grow in the sea.

set·tler (set′·lər) n. A person who moves to a new place that has few or no people.

shal·low (shal′·ō) adj. Not deep.

shel·ter (shel′·tər) n. Something that covers and protects.

shiv·er (shiv′·ər) v. To shake from being cold.

sieve (siv) n. A utensil made of wire mesh or metal with many small holes, used for straining.

sloe (slō) n. A small, sharp-tasting, plum-like fruit.

slope (slōp) n. Rising or falling ground; a hill.

snow·drop (snō′·drop′) n. A white flower that blooms in spring.

spar·row (spar′·ō) n. A small singing bird of a dull brown color.

spend·thrift (spend′·thrift′) n. A person who spends wastefully.

spi·der (spī′·dər) n. A small animal with two body parts, four pairs of walking legs, and no wings.

splin·ter (splin′·tər) n. A sliver; a thin piece split off a larger part.

spout (spout) n. The opening through which a drink is poured.

square (skwâr) n. An open space

near the center of a town and bounded by streets on all sides.

stalk (stôk) *n.* The main part of a plant.

starve (stärv) *v.* To die from hunger.

stool (sto͞ol) *n.* A seat like a king or queen's throne.

stun (stun) *v.* To make unconscious or unable to act.

sur·vive (sər·vīv′) *v.* To remain alive.

sus·pi·cious (sə·spish′·əs) *adj.* Distrustful; suspecting.

swiv·el chair (swiv′·əl châr) *n.* A chair that turns on its base.

tame (tām) *adj.* Not wild.

tan·go (tang′·gō) *n.* A ballroom dance from Latin America.

taunt (tônt) *v.* To challenge or make fun of in a mocking way.

tem·per·ate (tem′·pər·it) *adj.* Mild.

tem·per·ate for·est (tem′·pər·it fôr′·ist) *n.* A woods where many trees lose their leaves in the fall.

thick·et (thik′·ət) *n.* A thick growth of plants.

thyme (tīm) *n.* A garden herb used in cooking.

tick·er tape pa·rade (tik′·ər tāp pə·rād′) *n.* A traditional hero's welcome in which ribbons of paper are thrown from buildings as the hero passes by.

tide pool (tīd po͞ol) *n.* A pool of sea water left by the sea.

tilt (tilt) *v.* To lean or slant. *n.* A leaning position.

tor·na·do (tôr·nā′·dō) *n.* A funnel-shaped cloud of whirling winds that moves over land destroying anything in its path.

tri·al (trī′·əl) *adj.* Test; tried out.

tum (təm) *Informal.* Short for *tummy. n.* Stomach.

tu·tu (to͞o·to͞o) *n.* A short skirt worn by a ballerina.

un·yield·ing (ən′·yēl′·ding) *adj.* Firm; steady; unbending.

Vic·trol·a (vik·trō′·lə) *n.* A record player.

waltz (wôlts) *n.* A ballroom dance.

web (web) *n.* A fine net woven by some spiders to catch food.

wind·mill (wind′·mil′) *n.* A building with sails on a wheel that are turned by the wind.

wiry (wīr′·ē) *adj.* Being thin and able to move easily.

wool·ly (wo͞ol′·ē) *adj.* Like wool from a sheep's coat.

yam (yam) *n.* A root, like a sweet potato, that is eaten.

yarn (yärn) *n.* A string of fiber used for weaving, knitting, or making thread.

zig·zag (zig′·zag) *n.* A series of short, sharp turns or angles.

Sounds and Letters

The letters **a**, **e**, **i**, **o**, and **u** are vowels. One of these letters is found in almost every word. Each vowel has a short vowel sound. Say each word. Listen for the short vowel sound.

/a/ as in **yam**	page 296	/o/ as in **box**	page 65
/e/ as in **legs**	page 67	/u/ as in **stuck**	page 76
/i/ as in **six**	page 67		

Each vowel has a long vowel sound. Sometimes the vowel sounds are spelled in several ways. Here are the five vowel sounds with examples of their different spellings. Say each word. Listen for the long vowel sound.

/ā/

ai as in **daisy**	page 36
eigh as in **eight**	page 94
ay as in **crayon**	page 137
a–e as in **shade**	page 240
ey as in **they**	page 27

/ē/

ee as in **knees**	page 65
ea as in **leaf**	page 65
y as in **Harry**	page 70
ie as in **field**	page 79

/ī/

i–e as in **wire**	page 62
igh as in **right**	page 68
y as in **fly**	page 69
ind as in **winding**	page 306

/ō/

o–e as in **Mole**	page 45
ow as in **show**	page 66
o as in **no**	page 68
oa as in **coating**	page 76

/ū/

u–e as in **computer** page 333
ue as in **fuel** page 333
eu as in **Eugene** page 13
u as in **United States** page 216

Sometimes two letters blend together to make one sound. Here are two vowel combinations and four consonant combinations. Say each word. Listen for the new sound.

/aw/

aw as in **claws** page 86
au as in **because** page 46
al as in **calm** page 47
augh as in **daughter** page 167
ough as in **thought** page 168

/oi/

oi as in **oil** page 76
oi as in **voice** page 320
oy as in **joy** page 209
oy as in **boy** page 306

/sh/

sh as in **dash** page 57
sh as in **shiny** page 66

/ch/

ch as in **kitchen** page 59
ch as in **chewing** page 296

/th/

th as in **thank** page 62
th as in **hundredth** page 205

/wh/

wh as in **wheels** page 309
wh as in **whispered** page 58

F 0
G 1
H 2
I 3
J 4

8
9
0

416